CHRISTINE HART

The Devil's Daughter

THE DEVIL'S DAUGHTER

This book first published November 1993 in the United Kingdom
by NEW AUTHOR PUBLICATIONS LTD
Halt Gate House, Hullbridge Road,
South Woodham Ferrers, Essex. CM3 5NH
Tel/Fax: 0245 320462

Where certain events contained in this book are investigateable by
the publishers they have proved to be correct. The Author agrees
that all contents are true and as stated according to her recollection
and accepts full responsibility for the contents.

Typeset by S.O.S. Copying and Business Services,
Leigh-on-Sea, Essex. Tel: 0702 714706

Printed and bound by Redwood Books,
Trowbridge, Wiltshire, England

Editor: Guy Nathan

Foreword: Colin Wilson

Cover Design: Joe Elgie

Agents: The Jeffrey Simmons Agency, London
Tel: 071 235 8852

Publicity: Midas P.R., Wandsworth, London
Tel: 071 731 5948

ISBN 1 897780 90 7

U.K. Price : £5.99   U.S.A. : $9.50c

ACKNOWLEDGEMENTS

Special thanks to Colin Wilson for his 'idea' to write this book.

My affection and gratitude to Robert 'Barney' Barnett and his Mother, Clare and her family for opening their home to me whenever I have most needed it.

To the Hart family for accepting me as their daughter and giving me a home . . . . Also Guy Rodway and all the staff and kids at Olympic House. Thanks to Deidre Morgan, Susan Barr, Maya Bagnall, and the many others that I remember but haven't the room to mention. To David Lindsay for his 'Voyage to Arcturus' and for its influence and for the lyrics of Bob Dylan.

Finally, Jeffrey Simmons, my Literary agent, for his belief in me as a writer and my Editor, Guy Nathan of New Author Publications.

Christine Hart . . 1993

CONTENTS

PART ONE

PART TWO

The Devil's Daughter

PREFACE

Christine Hart was brought up in an orphanage. She regarded herself as the loneliest girl in the world, and fantasised that her father was a pop star until she was told, very unkindly and on very uncertain evidence, that he was an infamous criminal.

She came to believe that her father must be the loneliest man in the world, and that perhaps he was Ian Brady, the notorious Moors murderer.

Probably in search of a father figure, she started a remarkable relationship with him by correspondence, which eventuated in her actually meeting him.

Her world collapsed about her when a national Sunday newspaper announced on it's front page that she was Brady's daughter. With practically no money, she fled to New York City, where she survived (without a work permit) in a sort of limbo, in quite extraordinary circumstances.

This is Christine's story in her own words.

FOREWORD

Readers of this book may feel as I did after reading an earlier and less complete version: that it has left an important question hanging in the air. I found myself confronting that question soon after Easter 1990, when the author arrived unannounced at my front door. In fact, I was in bed at the time, and it was not until the next morning that my wife told me: 'Someone came to see you late last night.' I groaned; I hate unannounced visitors. 'I hope you told him I won't see people without an appointment?' 'It was a girl - rather a pretty blonde girl. She claims she knows Ian Brady. In fact, she left one of his letters.'

I looked at the handwritten letter. It was obviously genuine. And as I read it, I could see why she felt it would interest me. Brady talked about 'outsiders', and it was clear that he knew my work.

A bell rang in my head. I had recently written an account of the Moors murders in a book called The Serial Killers, and had been looking through my collection of press cuttings on the case. And I recalled the front page of newspaper with a picture of a pretty blonde. I went and looked it out. The story was about a correspondence between Ian Brady and a girl called Christine Hart, and the possibility that she might be his daughter. When I showed my wife the picture she said: 'Yes, that's her.'

She was staying in a nearby hotel. I was due to go to our local village to do a television interview on the quay. When I rang the hotel, I was told that she was still in bed, so I left a message saying that I would collect her in half an hour. When I arrived, she had still not appeared. Finally, after keeping me waiting a quarter of an hour, she came downstairs - an attractive blonde in her mid-twenties, with a London accent. I told her I was late and we could talk on the way to Mevagissey. As soon as we'd cleared away the preliminaries of introduction I asked her why she

1

wanted to see me. She explained that she had entered into correspondence with Ian Brady because she was fascinated by the case. Now she wanted to write a book about it, and wanted my help and advice.

My advice was that she probably didn't have enough experience to write a book about the Moors case. But as she talked to me about her appalling childhood, and her subsequent life, it became clear that she probably <u>did</u> have the material for a remarkable autobiography - if she could write it.

In fact, during the next few months, the pages of a scrawled but oddly legible manuscript that came through the post left me in no doubt she could write. She wrote as easily and naturally as she talked. The main question now was: had she the patience and application to finish it?

A few weeks later I received a letter from Ian Brady's solicitor, Benedict Birnberg. It seemed that he had got wind of the projected book, and had heard that I intended to collaborate with Christine. He wanted to point out that she would not be allowed to quote any of the letters she had received from Brady. I replied that I had no intention of collaborating with Christine on a book, and that as far as I knew she had no intention of quoting Brady's letters. I also commented:

'Christine talked very lucidly and interestingly about Brady and about herself, and there could be no doubt that she found him so interesting because she saw him as a kind of male version of herself. Like most people, I feel pretty horrified by Brady's crimes; but I must admit that what she said 'humanized' him and made him seem less of a monster. I had just finished my book on the serial killer, and her comments gave me new insights. (We <u>have</u> to understand the serial killer if we are to do anything useful about the problem.) This is why I feel that she should at

2

least try to write a book centering on <u>how</u> she became so obsessed by Brady.'

The only sentence I felt dubious about in retrospect is the one about Christine seeing Brady as a male version of herself. This is an oversimplification. It would have been more accurate to quote Dick Dudgeon in Shaw's <u>Devil's Disciple</u>, who explains how, in the gloomy puritanical household in which he was brought up, he began to feel that if his mother hated the Devil so much, there must be some good about him; thereafter, he used to pray to the Devil for comfort. The young Aleister Crowley came to identify with the Great Beast in Revelation for the same reason.

Christine had had a miserable upbringing, and she had developed into a typical social rebel. From her point of view as a 'reject', society seemed stupid and self-absorbed. A hint from a social worker that her real father had been a notorious criminal led her to suspect that it might have been Ian Brady - the time and the place both fitted. She entered into a correspondence with Brady, who told her that she was a female version of himself. Brady recognizes that he may well be her father, but as their correspondence developed, she came to see him as a fellow rebel in revolt against stupidity, hypocrisy and complacency.

There was a sense in which she was correct. Brady had also been brought up by foster parents - his father, a journalist, had died before he was born. Highly dominant, resentful of the Glasgow slum in which he spent the first ten years of his life, he committed his first burglary at the age of nine. He made his first appearance in a juvenile court at the age of thirteen, and was bound over. When he appeared again at sixteen, with nine charges against him, he was placed on probation on condition that he join his mother and stepfather in Manchester. He worked in the fruit market, and there made the mistake of helping a friendly lorry driver to load some stolen lead. And since he was on probation, the judge threw the book at him and gave him two years in Borstal. He was outraged; he regarded the sentence as totally unfair. And when he emerged from Borstal - still on probation - he had resolved to try and make a fortune as a criminal, then retire to South America, or somewhere of the sort. He felt that society 'deserved' it.

It is impossible to doubt that Brady was highly intelligent. He had always haunted public libraries, and in Manchester he read Nietzsche, Dostoevsky, Sade, Mein Kampf and my own Outsider. He identified with Raskolikov of Crime and Punishment and Stavrogin of The Possessed. He had also, since his early teens, been preoccupied with a curious death-mysticism. The journalist Fred Harrison describes how, on his way to his first job interview, Brady felt dizzy and stopped in the doorway of a newsagents shop. 'And there it was, a green, warm radiation, not unattractive to the young man who clutched his head to try to steady himself. The features were unformed, but still recognizable. Ian knew that he was looking at the face of death.'

Now, in the office where he worked, a new typist named Myra Hindley became violently infatuated with him. At first indifferent, he finally took her out for the evening. Soon they were lovers. A curious and morbidly intense relationship developed - both have commented that they became virtually telepathic. For Myra, it was like religious conversion - in fact, the easiest way of understanding the change that came over her personality is to think of the female disciples of the America 'messiah' Charles Manson, or the members of the sect who died at Waco with David Koresh. For someone like Brady - who experienced no sense of kinship with his fellows - it was a dangerous situation to be in. The sense of finally ceasing to be alone, the sense of dominance over a partner, removed all inhibitions. The components of nitro-glycerine. The subsequent explosion, the Moors murders, still (as

Fred Harrison put it) 'haunts the psyche of the nation.'

Brady commented to Harrison that after two years of murder, 'I felt old at 26. Everything was ashes. I felt there was nothing of interest - nothing to hook myself on to. I had experienced everything.' This strange sense of bewilderment, of coming to the end of their tether, has been recorded of many serial murders.

Under the circumstances, it is not easy to see how Christine came to regard Ian Brady as a kind of second-self. But I think the second part of the book enables us to understand it. In New York, she was even more alienated than Brady in Manchester; she also began to experience hallucinations, including the 'face of death.' At this time Brady's letters seemed a lifeline to sanity, and his attitudes and ideas seemed to reflect her own. When talking to me about this foreword, she emphasized the importance of these ideas - about the 'higher self', the need to find a new kind of consciousness. She even quoted to me a passage from my novel about a serial killer The Glass Cage - which Brady had recommended her to read - in which the hero talks about the mystic's attempt to break beyond the walls of 'ordinary consciousness', into the jungle that lies beyond, and explains that drugs and drink are one way of making us aware of this jungle, while murder is another. 'When people go insane, they are actually seeing deeper than most of us. Insanity isn't based on delusion; it's based on truth.' And he goes on to talk about the very small percentage of 'real murderers', the rebels who kill for self-gratification.

Perhaps the simplist way to underline the point is to refer to the work of the French philosopher, Michel Foucault. In his Madness and Civilization, Foucault argues that madness has been somehow 'domesticated' by civilization. In doing this, the aim of 'authority' has been to keep it at arm's length, to place it literally beyond the pale.

Apparently one of Foucault's main inspirations was an extraordinary evening in 1947 when the actor Antonin Artaud, who had just come out of an asylum, read weirdly surrealistic poems in a theatre. He read in a hoarse, almost inaudible voice, often clawing the air; sometimes he sobbed; sometimes there were long pauses. At first the audience was embarrassed; then, gradually, they came to understand that Artaud was not trying to 'entertain' them; he was baring his soul to them, and in so doing, giving them a practical demonstration of his idea of the 'theatre of cruelty', where the audience is drawn into a kind of horrified participation. Like the hero of Barbusse's novel Hell, which I quote in the first chapter of The Outsider, Artaud felt that he 'saw too deep and too much.' He objected to being treated as a madman when he felt that other people could not see what he could see. Foucault's book is a plea for the recognition of these frightening dimensions of consciousness.

This, it seems to me, is the key to what Christine Hart is saying. She is trying to explain how it is possible for a basically 'normal' person to feel so totally alienated that everything about society and 'normality' seems to her a sham. She wants to shout this insight from the rooftops. I cannot accept her estimate or empathize deeply with her point of view - or Artaud's, for that matter; but I acknowledge the power with which she expresses it. Anyone who wants to pursue this argument in all its philosophical complexity should read Foucault's Madness and Civilization. But it seems to me that Christine, writing with the simplicity of a frustrated but very perceptive child, does it far more straightforwardly and far more effectively.

Colin Wilson, 1993

6

INTRODUCTION

IAN STEWART BRADY was sentenced to three consecutive life sentences for the murder of seven young people back in 1966.

He was jailed with his lover Myra Hindley for the murders. All the children were ritually murdered and buried on the Yorkshire Moors. He serves out his life long imprisonment in a top security asylum for the criminally insane.

With information and a sincere premonition, Christine Hart started to correspond with him. After many years, finally in 1987 when she was 23 years old, she met him.

THIS IS HER STORY.

PART ONE

I don't want to give anyone a bad idea of my foster parents. They were good people and they were the only parents I knew. And they fostered me when I was six years old from the orphanage, and I took their name. Then I had two names, my real name and the name my new parents gave me.

Ian used to say that I was unlucky to be picked by them. And I'd say I wasn't unlucky. I haven't had a life filled with horror and I wasn't locked up or made to live in the garden shed. I was only not loved. People can survive without love. Children can survive without love. I've seen many that have and carry on doing so.

There are some though, that on emerging into this world and finding only emptiness and absence of love, retreat mentally back into the world they have come from.

These children don't seem to belong in the world at all. Their natural and happier habitat is the inner world that they have retreated into and they are different from the rest. Withdrawn. Not really with you, like a kind of absent mindedness or not all there; and they are 'not all there'. They live with one foot in this world and one foot in some other world. And when our kind, the unwanted and the unloved retreat inwards, sometimes we back too far and by accident slip into a place that has a reality that is just as real or more real than this world.

And living in this different environment, this different consciousness, or level of consciousness, we have the ability to become Gods or even Devils. And all by an accident of birth.

There once was a baby girl, she was barely six months old and lived with her mother and two other little babies, her brother and her sister. One day the unmarried mother decided she couldn't cope with all the children. And she picked up the baby girl and took her in her pushchair along to the place where people put unwanted children, the orphanage, then turning, she quickly walked away. And as the young child's screams echoed in her ears her pace quickened and she never came back. The young child left alone with strangers in the cold dormitory like institution and without its mother, quickly retreated into a much warmer inner world inside herself.

The accident of birth.

She was just a baby. It was then 1964.

In the orphanage we'd have selection days where we'd line up in a line and people would walk up and down and decide if they wanted us or not. I was six years old around then. The children around my age stood no real chance of being picked for adoption. Everyone wanted the babies so they could mould them. Mould them into being like themselves. With older children they had no chance of doing that, and these people were only there because they couldn't have their own kids, not because they just wanted to love the unwanted ones.

Even as a baby, I hadn't been adopted. My natural mother hadn't signed me over for adoption. Instead she visited me once or twice a month, or so I was told. Mary her name was, and she'd bring me sweets and chocolate and toys and some new clothes to wear. She stopped coming then around the time I was six years old, and moved away from the area. When the staff couldn't trace her, they decided to let me be fostered out. So I was made to join the others on Sunday afternoons and stand in the line while all the adults walked up and

9

down and stopped to talk to us. Some of the others used to cry if they weren't picked, and I remember some of them would scream and grab onto the legs of the people as they tried to leave.

I don't really remember much about what life was like there, I remember always lining up for things, like bath-time and meal times, always so many lines. There was a little boy there who was my best friend, Adrian. He'd sleep next to me, and he'd whisper to me at nights, and we'd often sleep in each others beds, then jump out in the morning before we got told off about it.

I remember the time when I first saw my foster father. He was the tallest, handsomest man who came in there. He had dark swept back hair and kind pale blue eyes. And he took me, just took me by the hand to go off and live with him, and I remember being so surprised that I forgot to look for Adrian and I forgot to say goodbye and only remembered later when I was in the car with the man, on my way to my new home.

It was strange living there. There were so many different noises at night time that I didn't recognise. I remember the bed. It was big and soft, and the bedroom, the bedroom I had all to myself was like a princesses bedroom, it was painted in a beautiful pink. with toys, cuddly toys that I didn't share with the others, they were all mine in my own room.
After I'd been there a while, they taught me to answer to my new name Christine, not Tracey as I had been called at the orphanage. And I had a new second name, Hart, like theirs. They had decided to adopt me, and when they could contact my mother they would make my new name a legality. I found it hard to call them mum and dad at first, but eventually it just seemed natural and I accepted them as my mum and dad forever.

And it was for four years I lived there that seemed like forever, and I was ten when, one day, my foster father took me by the hand and took me back to the orphanage. All those years, that had seemed then, like a lifetime.

The Harts couldn't look after me anymore, I was too much trouble. I never laughed, and they had told the staff they thought that I was autistic and needed some sort of special care; and they couldn't give it to me.

The adoption had gone ahead two years previously, so I was back in the orphanage but with a new name, Christine Hart, and an old name I could use if I wanted, Tracey Mary Sweeney.

I think I thought a lot about my foster father. I didn't remember my mother very much except her shouting at me once, I don't remember what about, but her shouting a lot. But I'd cry at nights remembering my foster father and the way I'd sit on his knee. I remember when I was eight or nine we'd go along to yearly parties they had at the orphanage and I'd hold on tightly to my Daddy's hand. I did love him, very much, and I felt very warm and secure with him, he was mine and my favourite place was perched on his knee. No one could take him away. His love was secure or so I thought. It was at the party I realised that that wasn't necessarily true.

It was a sight I never forgot and I recoiled in horror when I'd turned to see my Dad with another little girl sat up on his knee, holding her in the same way that he held me; lovingly.

"We'll find some other little girl, put you back and take her, one not so miserable, more fun and full of life", my mother had chastised in the car on the way down when I hadn't smiled or spoken for the whole journey.

What if that were true I thought to myself as I witnessed the scene of closeness. And I felt a surge of such a powerful emotion. It kind of filled me, and gave me a push inside, a sort of anger. It was the feeling of possessiveness and jealousy. Afterwards that was never to leave me. It was always there to leap out at me

11

when I least expected it. To whisper its frightening thoughts into my mind and to show me scenes of pain before they happened. The jealousy was born and grew as I grew; each day bigger and stronger.

There's not much else I remember about my time at the Harts', except that I was very happy and it was the time I lived as a princess for a while. Safe, rescued, rescued from the cold place and bought to a soft pink room where I lived and I was me.

Being back in the orphanage I had to change primary schools and trouble started just as soon as I got there. They'd pick me up in a big yellow bus with the councils name on it. I was the only one from our home that went to that particular school as it was a Catholic school and I'd been brought up so far as a Catholic so they wanted to keep it that way. But the other kids wanted to know why the new girl was picked up in a bus with the name written alongside, not met by their mummy or daddy like they all were. And so the teachers told them. And one of their parents must have told them what a bastard was, and the meaning of the word,illegitimate, because I learned these two new words and I learned that that is what I was. And sometimes in the playground I was surrounded by jeering and shouting children "You live in an orphanage, your mum didn't want you. You ain't got no home like us."

I didn't have any friends at school, I suppose I was too quiet, and at lunch times I'd sit in the corner on my own watching the other girls playing and pretend it didn't matter and eat my sandwiches so slowly that they'd last me until the bell sounded for the end of break.

A teacher called my social worker up to see her after school with a letter, 'She never smiles,' I heard her say, 'I've never seen such a melancholy child'.
But I was happy. Happy in a different world. One of books. I used to read at least one every two weeks. I'd devour the words in books like Half Magic and

Seven Day Magic and The Green and Bronze Mirror where the children in the story had adventures in another world, a world that ran parallel to ours, but wasn't really like ours.

My favourite book of that particular kind was called "A Wrinkle In Time", by Madeleine L'Engle. The other world in it was called "The Fourth Dimension." It was my favourite book and I read it and re-read it during the time in the orphanage. Then left it behind when I reached thirteen and had to leave. I was moved to an older children's home in Uxbridge, Middlesex; Olympic House. It was now 1977.

I remember the first day I went to Olympic House. I went straight from the orphanage in the social worker's large blue Rover. I sat nervously in the front seat, two carrier bags perched on my knees containing all my stuff, and I gripped onto them tightly. I'd waved goodbye to the orphanage staff and the other kids and bit hard down on my lip and tried not to cry. I'd heard that when you got to these places where the older boys and girls were, that you had to have a fight first to see if you were weak or strong; I was terrified of this because I couldn't fight at all, but I put on the tattiest clothes I could find and hoped they wouldn't hit me too, hard, but feel sorry for me instead. The social worker, Adrian, took me through Middlesex, to see Middlesex Lodge, the girls borstal. 'That's where you could've gone until we found a place for you, but luckily somewhere came up'. The huge borstal surrounded by a large barbed wire fence frightened me and the social worker slowed the car so I could get a closer look at it. 'That's where you'll go if you're a bad girl though, the lock up', he said solemnly as we drove on; I clutched my carrier bags even tighter. After about half an hour he drove up in front of a huge complex, new and made of red brick. It was fairly near to the orphanage where I was brought up, only ten or so miles away but it was in such a strange part of Uxbridge, I didn't fully recognise it and it was weird, like being on holiday or something.

After Adrian had dropped me there, he drove off almost straight away, and I was left standing in the huge brightly decorated reception area on my own. After I'd been standing there a while, a tall dark haired social worker appeared, and showed me the way to my room. It was Dave King who was in charge of the home. He smiled, kind eyes, but I felt lost.

My room was one of five rooms along a long white painted corridor, separated by a huge thick burgundy coloured reinforced door which led to the boys corridor, which also had five separate rooms and a large bathroom and toilet at each end.

I was shown into a room that day and then the door was closed behind me. I sat on the small single bed with its folded white cotton sheets and mustard yellow blankets. The white walls were covered in graffiti with thick black marker pen, a lot of it obscene, and the small sink in the middle of the room was full of ash and cigarette butts.

I unpacked my carrier bags, and sat on the bed. I didn't know whether to move or not so I just sat there and the daylight faded and it slowly grew dark outside before someone came and knocked at the door.

It was Eddie White, huge, blond and tanned with a body like a weight lifter. I thought at first that he must've been one of the staff there.

It turned out he was sixteen and he was one of the kids "You're new aren't you," he enquired?, "They told me to tell you dinner's ready, you have to be quick if you're hungry."

It was the first time I'd had the experience that I think is common in a lot of institutions. If you're hungry you have to grab it and eat it quick or someone eats if for you and you only have a certain time to eat then go and wash and dry up your plate in the kitchen. I'd always been a slow eater at the Orphanage, chewing every mouthful, but after I lived at Olympic House from when I was thirteen to when I was put out of care on my eighteenth birthday, and during those five years, I gobbled my food as fast as I could and I've never been able to shake myself of the habit and still eat now as if I'm being timed or am in some sort of race.

All the other children were sixteen when I'd first got there and the three years difference mattered a lot when you're that age.

They all thought that I was a baby. I wasn't invited into their tightly knit group of long talks in each others rooms and dancing in the front room to the records on the old second hand record player.

But I had my books and most of the time when not at school I'd be sitting in my room reading or I'd be down in the kitchen talking to Peggy, the old woman who came to cook the dinners, or the various black ladies that used to come in the morning and do the hoovering around the rooms. I got so friendly with Peggy the cook and she so friendly with me that I was allowed to go round, to her house and sometimes stay overnight in the small terrace where she lived by herself. Her husband was ill and he'd been hospitalized for years in the large Victorian built mental home in Hanwell, St. Bernards, and she would visit him every Sunday afternoon and sometimes she'd take me with her. I loved spending time with her and preferred it to the coldness of Olympic House, where I still hadn't made any friends.

Months passed there and then a year, and I'd gradually got to know the other kids who I lived with. There was Kerry, she had her pale ginger hair shaved close to her head and followed the skinhead cult. She wore huge Doc Martins boots and had been in care all her life, so she was the head of the girls' section, not really because of the length of time she had been there, but because if she didn't like you she'd break your nose.
She had a room next to mine and it was done out in purple and pink and had

15

two fluffy white rugs in the middle.

I was always jealous of those rugs, because my room was so tatty and empty, they would have gone nicely and warmed it up a bit.

She wasn't in all that much, she had a huge black boyfriend called Kelvin who was much older than her and who came to pick her up in a beaten up old silver Mercedes.

She'd been put in care by her parents who said they couldn't manage her as they had three other daughters. It was supposed to be temporary when she was a baby, but they never took her back. She didn't see them anymore, but I knew she knew where they lived and kept a framed photo of them hidden in her drawer.

Then there was Floyd, a tall black boy of seventeen, the unspoken 'head' of the boys' end whose room smelt of wood and spicy aftershave and who would blast out soul music from his record player all the time.

Floyd was hardly ever around and when he was he kept himself to himself preferring to mix with the black militants in Notting Hill, and smoke thinly rolled joints in the back room of a snooker club somewhere.

There were two other girls around that time besides Kerry, Julie and Baljit, and they were nearly eighteen and just about to leave so they didn't bother with me much.

Then there was Steve, a spotty seventeen year old and Martin another black boy who had just come from the 'Send' borstal. Nobody there really spoke to me, least of all the social workers who appeared to change nearly every other day and who mostly would sit in the staff rooms discussing things with each other. A lot of them had been to the same universities and they sat for ages reminiscing and talking about their different political beliefs.

I was still at school around this time, and the headmistress regularly called me into her office to ask me if I was happy and if I wanted anything. I remember once telling her I hated it at Olympic and that I needed some toothpaste.

Much to my embarrassment, the next day she handed me a Boots bag in the middle of the corridor in front of a load of people in my class. Inside was some toothpaste, a face flannel and a bar of purple lavender soap.

Most of the time after school I'd go round Susan Barr's house, my one friend from school, and I'd have tea with her and her mum and dad, but I gave up going after a while because the smell of chips cooking as I came in their doorway after school, the kitchen windows steamed up with the heat from the cooker and the smell of eggs and bacon reminded me of my own life at a proper home. And the memory cut through me like a kind of pain. Susan lived quite near to the people who had fostered me as a child, and after having tea at her house her father would normally give me a pound to get myself something and I'd use it as bus fare and go and stand at the corner of the road where I used to live and look over to what once had been my home. I'd watch from under the lamppost on the corner, and the lights were on and it would look all warm inside and I'd look at it and I'd wonder had I ever lived there or had it been some sort of dream? I would stand there for ages imagining I was still living there, inside, in my pink room.

The life at the home though was a fairly peaceful one, and usually kept to a kind of routine. Sunday was always wash day, where we would all take turns to wash our stuff in the big machine. The washing room was downstairs at Olympic, in the communal part. There was a television room, table tennis room and a huge kitchen. Then across from that the quiet room, the staff room, the staff rest room and the office where our files were kept under lock and key. The staff would work on a rota system and change at two o'clock in the afternoon.

None of them lived on the premises except for the officer in charge, Dave King, who lived with his wife and two children in the red house built on the side of the home.

In the mornings, five or so cleaners would come, mostly black women who would stand around for ages leaning on their hoovers, smoking and complaining about the mess we had made the night before, and then there was Peggy the cook, who I'd become so close to. She would take turns with another cook Maisie to do three days on and three days off, but on Sunday we would fend for ourselves.

Most of the time though the food was council bought school dinner type food. And every weekend two of the kids would be given ten pounds to go and get what was known as the 'supper stuff' and we'd go into town on the bus and buy crisps and ice cream and biscuits and treats from the supermarket and come back and put it in the cupboard to be used in the week for supper with our night drink. That was the general idea, but most of the time we'd all grab the stuff and eat it on the day it was bought.

I was there for nearly two years when one day I was sitting at tea and I heard all the others talking about the 'wolf boy'. He'd just come from another home and Floyd had found out that he'd raped a little girl, and had been to borstal for it. It seems they'd found this out at the previous home and the kids had made it difficult for him to stay there, so he'd been moved to Olympic House, and the other kids were fuming about it. They sat around the dinner table discussing it. One Saturday afternoon after all the dinner plates had just been cleared up, I sat quietly at the end of the table, watching Kerry admiringly as she smoked and spooned yogurt into her mouth in between puffs, and listened intently as they discussed the new boy.

They went on and on about him, he'd been called the 'wolf boy' at his old home because of his unkempt appearance and it was rumoured that he was homosexual or 'bent' as they put it as well, and they christened him 'ginger beer', the cockney rhyming slang for 'queer.'

The name stuck and Mark Townfield was to be known as 'Ginge' during his whole painful stay at Olympic House. He spent his first week in bed the whole time, and no one really saw him. He had the room at the end of the boys' corridor, a sparsely decorated box room with no curtains and yellow stained walls and a single bed. The first thing I noticed on approaching his room was the smell; it was a foul dank cabbage like smell or like rotting stale cake a sort of sweet and sour odour.

Kerry and I went down to his room and peered in through the keyhole. All we could see was masses and masses of dark brown animal-like hair on the pillow case and his thin frame outlined beneath the sheets.

A few days later I saw him, he was sitting in the wash room wrapped in a towel, watching a red track suit spin round and round in the otherwise empty washing machine. I later learned that it was all he had.

I watched him for a while without him noticing; his hair was everywhere and there was masses of it, all thick tangled and matted and it looked as if he hadn't combed it in ages. He was about five foot four in height, sallow skinned, a sad lost look about him, brown eyes and a small downturned mouth. He was about my age, and when I saw the talon like fingernails, I knew where the others had got the nickname 'wolf boy' from.

I found out Mark's history by accident one day, when they left the door of the staff room open whilst they were talking.

Dave King was explaining to the others Mark's life before he was put in borstal for raping the young girl. . . .

Before he was born his mother had had an affair with a married man. Mark was a result of that affair and Mark's 'step' dad resented him deeply. Then, Mark's mother died and her husband re-married again, this new wife giving birth to two little girls. Both the daughters looked like angels; blond, pale skinned and beautiful.

Mark wasn't blood related to either parents and both of them hated him. He was told to stay away from his two sisters and made to do most of the housework when he came in from school. Most evenings his father would beat him bloody with a hard leather belt with a silver buckle on the end of it and Mark's back was badly scarred because of this.

In the end twelve year old Mark had taken an overdose of paracetamol and drunk some household bleach in an effort to kill himself but his 'father' saved him and after he came out of hospital put him into the care of the authorities. He hadn't taken to care very well, and he'd been bullied a lot because of his small size. Frustrated over this and for whatever reasons, he'd attacked a girl five years younger than himself after school one day. The girl said he'd tried to rape her and Mark was sentenced to two years in borstal.

After borstal there had been numerous children's homes and assessment centres where he had also been bullied. He'd never been taught personal hygiene and cleanliness by his parents and a lot of the time had been made to sleep in the garden shed. This neglect accounted for bullying was Mark's strange appearance, like a wolf-boy, and also for the fact that he was very shy and nervous and didn't have the confidence to mix well with others.

I remember him during his first few months at Olympic House, and I remember how I used to watch him a lot of the time.

The other boys would beat him up on an almost daily basis, or if there was an observant social worker on duty, they'd just go up to his room and urinate on his bed and pour tomato sauce between the sheets and up the walls.

His appearance improved though, when one day, they jumped on him and cut his hair, then shaved it off bald with the aid of a bic razor. For the first time you could actually see his face, and he didn't look that strange, as the skinhead cult was quite the fashion.

But still, he cut a strange figure around the place, always alone, never talking, with that red track suit, and some old training shoes he had on his feet.

After he'd been there for a while, I tried to talk to him. He refused at first so I'd catch him as he came out of the bathroom, his hair soaking wet and his thin frame wrapped in an old bath towel, and I'd haul him by the arm along the girls corridor and into my room and make him sit in front of my old record player I had rescued from the quiet room downstairs and I'd comb his hair and blow dry it for him.

He'd sit silently during these sessions or sometimes he would pick out a record and put it on. Always Bob Marley and always the song 'Could You Be Loved'.

It was during the school summer holidays that Mark's 'father' came to the home. His wife had gone into hospital, and he needed help to look after the twins.

He told the staff he'd decided he wanted to have Mark back to live with him again, but it was obvious to everyone there that Mark's 'father' just wanted him back to help with the housework. Mark didn't see it that way. He worshiped his father and he thought that this was his 'father' admitting after all these years that he loved him.

Anyway, as we all thought, when his wife came out of hospital after three weeks, his 'father' gave Mark the beating of his life with his belt and Mark was sent back to the empty room at the end of the corridor.

21

I used to think I was so good, braving the comments like "Oh don't you mind the smell?" when I'd take him in my room to do his hair.

But that's all I did. All I did for him was do his hair. They'd all get at him, all the boys from our home and drag him out of bed at two or three o'clock in the morning and give him an ice cold bath or take him into one of their rooms and give him a beating. The next day, his face and eyes would be purple and swollen where they had been kicking, and beating it most of the night.

Then, one night they came and took him; five uniformed and two plain clothed police. They kept saying to him "You filthy bastard" as they dragged him naked out of bed. A young girl was raped and the description fitted Mark. He was taken to Feltham Borstal and word went out that after the trial he would be sent for an indefinite period to Rampton because they said he was mentally disturbed.

And I remember the day I heard this, shortly after he'd been taken away, I walked upstairs to his room. It did smell, his bed with the stained sheets and little else. He never had anything apart from that tatty red track suit he used to wear - and those holed, dirty white trainers. Not much for a teenager.

I opened one of the drawers casually, there was a note pad in there; it looked like one of the staff pads; he must've nicked it I suppose. I flicked through the pages to see if he'd written anything on it and I saw written on a page, a note 'Christine is my mummy, I love her', and I was taken aback I said aloud, in a voice of disgust, 'Oh how stupid, that's so childish', and then I leant my head on the wall and sobbed.

Time passed and after a while nobody mentioned Mark any more. Most of the time I kept out of the others' way. I used to listen to them playing music all the time and in each others' rooms laughing and joking, but I didn't mind; at least they weren't hurting me in any way.

The social workers didn't show much interest in many of the kids and tended to keep to themselves, chatting in the staff-rooms. I never knew how they managed to write the 'blue book', a diary on what all the kids got up to each day; there would be a note next to each of our names. And then there was the red book which was kept under lock and key with our personal files, and it was a day to day assessment on our personalities and how we behaved, and how we were progressing.

It was while I was at Olympic House that for some unknown reason, I began for the first time to be interested in my roots. I was about fourteen or fifteen around then and the opportunity soon availed itself to me.

One day, one of the social workers had been looking at the files. Leaving the file cabinet open, (she'd been called away to the telephone on the residents phone in the hallway), I saw my chance and flicked though till I found my file, stuffed it up under my jumper and went running upstairs with it.

I had a great big fat file. "Emotionally deprived" they'd called me and I remember feeling like a freak when I read it. I found out my real mother's name was Mary. The strange lady who'd visited me when I was small, and I found my birth certificate with my real name on it, Tracey Mary Sweeney. Where it said 'name of father', there was just a blank line.

I figured that it must have been some sort of a mistake and with the information I had arousing my curiosity, I went up to Somerset House to try to find out more. I found out her birth date and ordered both my birth certificate and hers. I was born in Epping in London. She had been born in Yorkshire. Then I checked my birth certificate, the one I'd received from Somerset House was exactly the same as the one they had in my file. My father's name had been omitted.

A line, where there should have been a name! Surely, everyone has a Dad! I remember being very uninterested in my mother. Maybe that thinking was a defence because I couldn't get it out of my mind that it had been her who had given me away, and her hand that had written that line, where she should have put the name of my father. I mean, why? Why did she do it? Maybe it had to be a secret. Maybe it was someone famous, a pop star or a film star who had to be kept anonymous. My imagination ran wild!

The following week I asked the staff question after question, and badgered the friendlier ones into trying to find out for me. One of them, tall, frizzy ginger haired Doug seemed to take an interest in me.

He was new to our home and he smoked long thin roll ups using that dark liquorice coloured paper; he reminded me of Clint Eastwood because of this, so I warmed to him when he'd singled me out for attention.

After confiding in him about my interest in who my father was, he told me he'd ask discreet questions with the other staff.

Two days later he'd come into my room in the morning as I lay in bed, sat next to me and held my hand. I jumped up, "Well, well, did you find out?"

I looked at him expectantly, and then the excitement turned to a dread. He looked upset for some reason "Well I did find out a little for you" he started, "I know you've been fantasizing that he's a famous pop star or a film star but I'm afraid he wasn't . HE WAS AN INFAMOUS CRIMINAL, currently in prison," he went on solemnly "serving a long sentence and your mother didn't want anything to do with him because of his crimes, which I believe were very serious. That was the reason she gave the orphanage for not putting his name on the birth certificate. Your mother did, however, tell the people who ran the orphanage where she left you, much more about him."

Doug helped me compose a letter to the Matron there, and three months later an appointment was made for me to have a counselling session and then to be given the information about my birth.

It was a disaster from the word go. I resented the social worker straight away who sat there playing God and holding onto a buff coloured file containing details of my life and 'deciding whether or not to give them to me. Anyway, I lost my temper. After an hour of her asking me "Why I wanted to know", as if it wasn't obvious, I shouted at her, "Are you going to bloody tell me or not?"

And that was that.
"Too immature to handle the information" she told Doug.

That made it worse, I built it all up in my mind: It must be terrible. The truth could kill me. Maybe he'd actually even killed somebody or maybe even loads of people. And he must have been really notorious, or there would have been no need for her to keep his name a secret.

One afternoon, I spent three hours in the true crime section of the local library. I was looking through all the books. Murderers Who's Who, The Encyclopedia of Crime. It began to sicken me. Pale faced people and descriptions of ugly murders, I was flicking through and then I found it, or should say, saw it. The photograph. The photograph of a man who didn't look like a man, he looked like a young boy, almost. He looked so out of place amongst the corrupt faces of the murderers, next to him, his photo was printed. He looked no different to them. Innocent, whereas they looked guilty.

Something about him, his face, touched something inside of me. It was almost, ... almost as if I knew him.

I let my gaze wander down the page until I found the writing about him. Ian Stewart Brady, imprisoned in 1966 for the murder of nine people. It didn't say much about him. His face, though; it seemed to ring so many bells in my mind. He wasn't who I was looking for but I wanted the photo of him. I stood behind one of the shelves in the library and ripped the page out of the book and stuffed it into my pocket. My heart was racing. I felt disorientated. I ran from that place to the safety of my room.

I stuffed the photo into the drawer. Later, when Doug was on duty, I showed it to him. He looked at it, then looked at me, puzzled, "Why are you pulling pictures of Ian Brady out of books. Surely he's not your father? I thought you went to the library to try and find out something about your father. Is his name the one given to you by the Matron?"

I continued to stare at the photo.

"I've got a book about him which .you can read if you like" Doug offered, "Yes, can I"? I asked eagerly. Doug promised to get me the book and when he was next on duty he handed it to me, and I started to work my way through it, slowly, with care, always trying to understand the man: read his thoughts, see his mind.

It was when I was nearing my seventeenth birthday and I'd have to come out of care that I started to worry. I'd seen the future of others who had left Olympic, stuck in bed and breakfasts or Tasman House, the doss house, where you went if you couldn't cope.

From time to time various people came to the home, prospective parents to foster us. Liz Merrow would always be front of the queue, she'd been in care all of her life; a fat blonde girl who had got a habit of smashing crockery and digging the pieces into her wrists; so she had loads of scar tissue on her wrists and arms.

She would always be waiting at the door if she knew some foster parents were coming, then she'd run around them making tea for them, all dressed up in her Sunday best.

Gillian and I, a fourteen year old coloured girl, would hide up in our rooms if we knew people were coming.

But I kept it a secret from her that I'd filled in a form myself and it was shown with my photo to all the people that came along. One evening, I was called down from my room and introduced to a man and woman that came from Slough. Mr and Mrs Walker. I shook hands and smiled at them and it was arranged that that Sunday I'd go to their house for tea and to meet their daughter. The following Sunday saw me dressed in my Sunday best and waiting in my bedroom for them to collect me. They were taking longer than I expected and my stomach was sick with nerves, so I went into Gillian's room and sat on the edge of her bed and began to talk to her about how I felt. As I was talking, I felt the bed shuddering under me and I couldn't see her face because it was buried beneath the sheets. I pulled back the covers, "Gillian Lewis, I don't see what's so bloody funny . . . . . . " I stopped. She wasn't laughing, she was crying, great big racking sobs going through her body.

"I don't want you to go and be fostered and leave me." I pulled her to me and we both hugged each other and cried.

I went without saying anything. I had to go, I couldn't stay. I couldn't face my future in a lonely bed and breakfast. I wanted a family to care for me and me for them, before it was too late.

The Walkers collected me and drove me out to their house in Slough. Their daughter wasn't around but I was shown my new bedroom and sat down and talked to them about my interests and how I hoped to get a job in the future.

I liked them and we got on well and I tried to hide my excitement and relief that I'd found a home from Gillian who eyed me sadly on my return.

I was supposed to wait a week before I went to the Walker's place for good. All the forms were signed and there was to be one preliminary meeting with the head of Social Services, Ian Miller and my original foster parents in order to sign me over. The meeting started, and the Walkers were there and my foster parents sat either side of the quiet room, and Doug my social worker sat beside me.

I remember thinking of my original foster parents,'Good, this will show them; someone else wants me, even if they don't'. I kept looking at them to see if they looked at me, or if maybe they regretted they hadn't kept me, way back then. But they didn't, they just kept their eyes front.

The meeting quickly got under way and to everyone's surprise Mr Walker stood up. "Look I think I should get this clear straight away" he began nervously, "We've been thinking this over, my wife and I, and we think, well she's been in an institution most of her life and she might have picked up some undesirable habits and pass them on to our daughter. We have to think of the influence on our daughter." His wife stood up with him, "We'd like to go now:" she added, "We don't think there is any point in staying."

They didn't look at me as they left and Ian Miller shot me a sympathetic look.

Doug leaned forward to squeeze my hand and I moved away, then turned and looked at him, embarrassed. My foster father, Mr. Hart, stood up. I could see this was going to be a short meeting. "We don't want her either; we're too old for any responsibility and we're sorry we can't have her", he said gruffly, not looking at me. "And I want to make a point", he added, "She's using my name, she's not my daughter, and I don't want her using my name."

I got up and walked slowly to the door, my legs were wobbly underneath me, then I walked up the stairs to my room. It was a few minutes later when Doug came up and sat on the bed beside me. My carrier bags were packed ready to go. I'd been expecting to leave that day with the Walkers. I started slowly to unpack them.

I took the book Doug had given me and handed it back to him removing the bookmark; the photo of Ian Brady. "He's like me", I said as I looked at the photo. "His mother put him in an orphanage, then he got fostered and they gave him back", I paused. "Just like me."

Doug reached out and held my hand and I pulled away immediately and sat there silently looking out the window.

"He's special isn't he? When I saw him I knew."

"Knew what?" asked Doug.

"I don't really know, I just knew something." Then I smiled at Doug and went and peeled off some cellotape and stuck the photo of Ian Brady onto the headboard of my bed.
"Look! How did you feel in the meeting?," Doug asked softly.

I ignored him.
"I really am there, aren't I ? The same as he was."

"Try to talk about the meeting, it will help you rather than keep in the pain", Doug pleaded.
"We live in the same place", I continued, "In a different world because you never accepted us into yours. As soon as we were born, we were put there. It's a different world and we're a different kind."

"Christine, you need to talk about how you feel or at least show some kind of emotion."

I wouldn't speak to him and eventually he got up and left me there. I sat in the same place until it got dark. I didn't cry then, I didn't really feel as if I was alone in the world. There was him, the man in the picture. We were the same kind, so that made us like a family, I didn't feel alone at all. There was someone else in the world who was like me, even though he'd been hung years ago, way back in the sixties.

I think that must have been it, the start of it all. The start of the craziness, or maybe if it had all stopped there,with a picture like 'Pictures of Lily', the song; just a man in a photo on the end of my bed. It would have all been alright, after all he was dead. He'd been hung for his crimes back in the sixties, hadn't he?

The man in the picture was just a dream, and if he'd stayed a dream maybe the craziness would have stopped, maybe I'd have grown up okay and have been married by now with babies and a normal life.

But from the day I saw that photo, it was like it was all 'meant to be', like I was following some sort of path or plan that had been mapped out for me.

I leaned very heavily on the comfort of him after that. I'd confide in him all my innermost secrets, and in the dark nights in my room, I'd shut my eyes and imagine what it would be like if we were friends, so close, and so devoted, only to each other, and all the loneliness, all the pain would vanish.
As in the song 'Picture of Lily', his picture helped me sleep at nights giving me the illusion that I had some company and a purpose in life. And he had become that company and Ian Brady had become that purpose.
It was two years later when I was nearly eighteen and soon had to leave Olympic House for Bed and Breakfast when I first found out that he hadn't been hung at all.

It was Christmas, Christmas 1978, and everybody had gone to homes that year and it was myself and another seventeen year old, Lloyd, the only ones they couldn't find foster parents for, Christmas Eve and we both sat opposite the social worker in charge, Ron, in the staff room.

We were both bored and restless, but Ron sat there ignoring us reading the paper, until he stopped and glanced over the top of it at me.

"Your friend's won the chess championship with John Stonehouse."

"What friend?" I said, bored.

"The one you've got pinned up on top of your bed."

I thought I was hearing things.

"He can't be alive", I looked at Ron in amazement, "He's dead, he was hung, it was years ago, the sixties, way back then."

"The death penalty had just been abolished. He just missed it and the sixties wasn't that long ago, he is very much alive and kicking, thank you madam" he finished angrily.

He passed me the newspaper and I looked at it in disbelief.

Ron ignored me and went on, "He's quite infamous you know, your friend, the Moors Murderers, they called them, him and his girlfriend Myra Hindley. He was only twenty six at the time of the murders, so he's only in his early forties now. Myra Hindley and he stopped corresponding to each other years ago."

"So he's on his own", I broke in excitedly. I went back upstairs to my room reading and rereading the article in the paper. Lloyd followed me. "It says here he's in solitary confinement, Rule 43", I said as I sat down on my bed, "How weird."

"Weird, why is it weird" snorted Lloyd derisively.

"Well, I mean, he's still alive" I said. I looked at the picture on the end of my bed. "Well it is weird, there he is alive and I'm talking to him and I've got his photo up here, and he's alive and just round the corner really in Wormwood Scrubs. I thought that we were in different times, and really, I'm alone, and he's alone, both in rooms like these."

Lloyd butted in "It's not really weird, it just means that you're crazy. Anyway you've got the best room here, mine looks more like a prison cell."

"I'm going to write to him anyway."

"And what will you say?" asked Lloyd.

"I don't know. Tell him he's not alone I suppose. He's not alone because I care about him, we've both got no-one and our sort have to stick together."

"Go on then, you write to him", Lloyd stated aggressively, "He'll just put the letter straight in the bin, he'll think you're crazy, and he's evil anyway, he won't give a damn about some stupid reject kid no-one else wants."

I chucked him out of my room and composed a letter.

"Dear Sir, I live at a place called Olympic House. It's a big children's home. I saw your picture in a book . . . . . . and so it went on, I told him about my hobbies and what I hoped to do when I left school and signed it, then left it in the post tray downstairs for the secretary to post.

I waited for days, then weeks, and then I resigned myself to the fact that Lloyd must have been right and he had thrown it away.

It was many years later when I found out the truth; The secretary had spotted who the letter was addressed to and had informed Dave King and he had told

Doug my social worker that it would be unthinkable for them to allow any sort of relationship to start. I sat outside on the swings in the garden, playing with the younger kids who had come over from the nearby orphanage. Not hearing, not knowing about the meeting he'd called. I saw them watching me from the window, but I didn't hear what they were saying.

"Could you imagine if the newspapers found out about that, someone in our care, writing to someone like that", Dave King said. "Anyway, it's destroyed, she won't be any the wiser and with no reply she will grow out of it. It's just a diversion, thinking about someone else's pain rather than her own. Identifying with him of all people, someone to love, an object person to focus on. There doesn't seem to be anyone else she identifies with. Imagine identifying with him though, I mean, out of all the people she could have picked. Bloody Ian Brady of all people.

"I think she thought he looked innocent" Doug laughed.

"I'd like to see her trying to explain that theory to the parents of the children he murdered" Dave King said angrily, "Anyway, I think that's put a stop to it. I don't think anyone need speak to her about it, I think if it's ignored it'll go away."

I tiptoed to the end of the girl's corridor, the window there was quite heavy and made a creaking noise as you opened it, so I pushed it open slowly so as to not wake anyone, then heaved myself up through it and onto the roof, then along the sloping roof, then I jumped down. As I jumped, my ankles weakened at the impact so I lunged forward onto my hands digging one of them into some jagged glass from a broken bottle that lay concealed in the grass.

I ran straight up the lane at the side of Olympic, in case I'd made a noise and woke anyone, and then checked my hand as soon as I'd made it out of sight. Blood was pumping from an inch long cut in the palm of my hand under the thumb and I started to feel faint at the sight of the oozing blood. I pressed the cut up against my jeans and soaked the blood up in them as I ran along the dark tree lined lane and up to the main road.

When I got to the main road, I started to continue walking, then, thinking again turned and stuck my thumb out. It wasn't long before a man in a white Volvo stopped, "You shouldn't be hitching lifts especially not at half past one in the morning."

I accepted his ticking off and got in the front seat beside him. He was going to Shepherds Bush near enough to my destination. I could walk the rest of the way. The driver introduced himself and said he had just finished work and I told him I lived up in White City and I was late home because I had stayed round my friends house too long. He was very talkative and when we got to Shepherds Bush decided to take me all the way to White City, to drop me off home.

"Du Cane Road I want", I announced loudly as we drew up to White City.

"Oh right near Wormwood Scrubs. Handy if you're a naughty girl;" he joked.
I got him to drop me off at the corner saying I'd walk the rest of the way and I walked up to the huge castle like red brick building with the white painted turrets. There was a huge brown wooden gate at the front and a 20 foot high wall that circled the whole of the prison with curled barbed wire perched on the top of it, to hinder any escape attempts.
I walked up to the huge gate. There was a bell on the side and a small door. I pushed the bell and a uniformed guard suddenly appeared from a side door.

"Which wing is Ian Brady in?" I asked him staring at him wide eyed.

He looked taken aback and stared at me in surprise. "How old are you?" he asked.

34

"Why? It's a school project. I know it's late, but I don't live round here, my Dad's round there in the car waiting. I was passing so I thought I'd ask."

He looked at me in disbelief, "D-Wing", he snapped then turned to walk inside.

I pressed the buzzer again, then, when he turned in anger, smiled at him, "Which wing is D-Wing?."

"The furthest on the right, now go away young lady." He turned away and I walked in that direction. .So that's where he was, D-Wing. All alone, locked up way up there in one of those turrets.

I made my way around to the side of the prison, and realised that if I made my way to the hospital nearby, I could double back on myself and stand right underneath the wing on a piece of waste land close by.

I think I must have stood there for hours, lonely and transfixed, looking up into blackness.

Time passed at Olympic House pretty uneventfully and soon it was my seventeenth birthday. Your seventeenth birthday is quite a milestone when you're in care. From the first day of your seventeenth, it is a preparation for your eighteenth birthday, when you will be cared for by the authorities no longer. And it frightened the life out of me!

I had been at Olympic for five years and the orphanage for ten years before that and I was, what they called, institutionalized, i.e. they have you pegged to either" go to bed and breakfast" or another institution - prison. Of the kids that were there when I was there, one is a prostitute, three are in prison, one hung himself and the other is a drug addict.

And that leaves me.

Olympic House had become my home and I couldn't bear to leave it.
And where would I go?

They held meetings to discuss my future and my foster parents were contacted.
Would they have me back, even on the terms of a lodger? The answer was a
firm, no!

In the end it was decided I went where every other kid goes when they are
eighteen and have spent all their life in council care. I went to live in a bed and
breakfast, a Social Services Hotel which was cheap and tatty and awful.

And then it was just me and the room; and the future looming ahead of me;
already at a social disadvantage. I was lonely. Surely, it couldn't get much
worse than this.

I'd wake up in the bed and breakfast and wonder what the hell was I doing
there. It frightened me. The whole place was full of drunken old men, and
lonely rootless people with nothing and no-one. And me, me too, I was one of
them. I thought of the years ahead of me, Christmases and Birthdays all spent
alone, and the rest of my life alone. If only "he" had written to me. I went round
to Olympic House daily to see if any letters had come for me. They hadn't.
I stuck the whole thing out for a year, while applying for jobs. I had no
qualifications and no experience. I got a job in a supermarket on the cheese
counter, then got sacked for lateness. Then another unskilled job in a factory.
Then another, until I stopped caring about anything.

The loneliness and emptiness and the fact no-one cared consumed my energy, I
felt broken before I had even started. I read in a book once someone who had
explained it like I felt it. It read:

> *'Everyone should be able to look back in their memory and be*
> *sure he had a mother who'd loved him, all of him, even his*

piss and shit. He should be sure his mother loved him just for being himself, not for what he could do, otherwise he feels he has no right to exist, he feels he should never have been born. No matter what happens to this person in life, no matter how much he gets hurt he can always look back to this and feel that he is lovable. He can love himself and he cannot be broken. If he can't fall back on this, he can be broken. You can only be broken if you're already in pieces. As long as my baby-self has never been loved then I was in pieces.'

I felt outside, and I felt the temperature was colder than I could withstand.

Just after a Christmas spent alone in that room, I decided I didn't want to live in the world where I didn't belong any more.

I took over 100 paracetamol, and eventually fell unconscious.

It was about a week later that I remember coming round in the hospital and opening my eyes, then thinking because of all the white that I was in heaven, and when it dawned on me, I cried and sobbed and started trying to pull out the tubes and things they had stuck up my nose, and the machines attached to various parts of my body.

Doug came to see me, and explained the landlady had come and knocked on the door, then tried to open it to clean the room and had found me. He told me that I'd been on a life support machine and I was lucky to be alive.

I turned my head away from him and allowed the tears to slide down my face. Soon I'd recover; then back to the room.

It was a week later when he came to see me again and bought me the news. The Social Services had been to see my foster parents, who were quite old now, but had asked them, as they had had me for such a long time as a child and I had been using their name, would it be possible for me to stay there.

Doug had gone round there and told them what had happened and told them that they wouldn't need to do anything for me, I'd just be like a lodger there and pay a weekly rent and get myself a job.

They were strict Catholics and I think they felt it their duty to help me. I don't know, but I felt at last that I had a chance. A life in a real home, again.

I remembered the similarity between what I'd read of Ian's life, how he had been returned to be a lodger with his real mother at seventeen, and how he had been practically ignored and only tolerated.

I was tolerated but it was a cold atmosphere and I felt they resented me there and I'd only been able to live there because of the overdose.

I spent most of my time in my room alone, and I would do myself tea and eat it on a tray up in my room. I cried a lot at nights, but he was there again, the man that looked like an angel, and I wrote a long letter I never posted, I just kept it in my handbag along with the picture of him.

It was like really, a new life for me. I was like a normal girl. A normal girl just like everyone else, with a proper name, a home, a family and living at home until I got married, maybe with a job in an office and some friends. At last I was fitting in, I was becoming like one of them.

Except for one thing, a photograph of Ian Brady I kept at the bottom of my handbag and the letters I'd written but hadn't posted. They remained there, dormant, like some sort of legacy from the past, shaking me or reminding me that there was something in me or about me that I was keeping hidden.

Life in a normal home and with a normal family came as a shock to me. After so many years in institutions, the quite large semi-detached seemed like a matchbox. I wasn't used to being able to go to the kitchen without asking the social worker for 'the keys' and I wasn't used to not shouting when I talked or using the bad language I'd picked up so quickly which I used so eloquently in the children's home.

My 'parents' lived mainly in the front room of the house, in front of the television most of the time, and my mother cooked dinner for my father and herself and they ate it in front of the television off trays perched on their knees. They didn't go out at all, and didn't drink or smoke; they were very strict Catholics and my father's sister was a nun, of the Daughters of St Paul in Rome.

I'd spend the majority of my time up in my room, reading mostly, laying on top of the bed flicking through the seven or eight library books I'd have out on a regular basis from the local library.
After looking around for a long time, and sick of the unskilled work I'd been doing, I found a job as an accounts clerk for Trusthouse Forte, based at Terminal Two, Heathrow Airport.

I wasn't allowed make-up or too showy clothes, so I dressed in the rather frumpy way of a spinster librarian or a forty year old school teacher with flat brown or black shoes and those thick orange brown tights. For doing this, I think they were pleased with me, but we'd never talk much. I just stayed in my room. But at least, in the bedroom at the top of the house, I was part of a family, and not alone. I had my photo, and <u>He</u> was there with me.

The emptiness and loneliness were still with me though, and only eased by the thought of the picture I had safely hidden away. The thought that he too, like me, and on the same night as me, sat somewhere alone, alone and empty. But not for long. One day I'd tell him about me, and he wouldn't be lonely anymore, and there'd be no pain anymore, not for either of us.

More letters - no replies.

Then one cold November morning, close to my 19th birthday, a letter from the governor of Wormwood Scrubs: 'Dear Miss Hart, I am afraid it is not possible for you to correspond with Mr Brady, as you did not know him prior to his sentencing.'

I wrote back and thanked the Governor for replying. At least it was something.

At work, I didn't make many friends. To be honest, so I spent most evenings and weekends in,my room reading, often, about the man whom I was convinced, was my father. Then I would return to work on Monday morning.

The small office was one of those old fashioned and dusty stock offices. There was the short balding and middle class Mr Kingdom, our office manager, two Indian girls and Flo an old woman near retirement age.

For most of the day we'd all be face down pens in hand making calculations and working out V.A.T. on the weekly returns or checking the stock records from the stores. The room would be deathly quiet as we all went about our daily duties sitting at our separate desks, the only sound being the clicking of the adding machine, as we added rows and rows of figures.

We would stop for morning coffee and our one hour lunch break when we would mostly eat sandwiches at our desk and I'd pull out the library book I'd be currently reading, and some of the others would be talking about what television programmes they watched the night previously or what diet they were on that particular week. Sometimes I could go into that office and not speak a word all day to anyone and then come home in the evening, make myself something to eat in the kitchen' then take it on a tray up to my room still not having spoken to anyone for the whole of the day. Sometimes, I felt that I was going out of my mind. Relief would come with "pills" induced sleep, and peace, with thoughts of the Man in the Picture.

Eventually the habit of not speaking became commonplace, and I'd blush to the roots of my hair if anyone spoke to me in a personal way or said hello to me whilst at work or walking home from work. I suffered agonies of shyness; and I'd creep around hoping that no-one would notice me or talk to me and jump three feet in the air if they did. I'm sure a lot of the time people thought that I was rude or arrogant or thought myself better than them, or too good to talk to them. When the truth was, I thought they were too good to talk to me. They terrified me. I felt like a robot or a machine. Carrying on a pretence of living. I felt that I wasn't being honest or I was sort of a fraud for some reason, and I couldn't really put my finger on why that was.

I'd worked there two years when the monotony of, my existence and the greyness of it began to weigh heavily on me. Nothing had any meaning, and I was so desperately, desperately lonely and empty inside. I felt that nothing was real. There was a cold dead feeling inside me, so much so, that I came to dread mornings and thought a lot about dying, and death and read a lot of poetry and books on the subject. I was beginning to be obsessed by it.

It seemed to me that dying was a beautiful thing and my favourite poet was Shelley and I read him and adored him, and loved the idea of the beautiful world he spoke about, the world after death, and the fact that this world is only · a preparation for it.
My favourite was *Adonais:*

Peace, Peace he is not dead, he doth not sleep,
He hath awakened from the dream of life
'Tis we, who lost in stormy visions keep,
With phantoms an unprofitable strife,
And in mad trance, strike with out spirits knife,
Invulnerable nothings - *We* decay,
Like corpses in a charnel; fear and grief,
Convulse us and consume us day by day
And cold hopes swarm like worms within our living clay.

I didn't know yet that the loneliness was coming to an end, and I was just about to find a friend. He'd been a long time in coming! He came in the rather huge shape of David. Twenty stone, large, hugely built sasquash monster, yet he was beautiful and we were to become inseparable.

I met him one night when I accompanied the girls from work when they went to a nightclub one Saturday.
I used to go to this nightclub every fortnight or so and I would tell my 'parents' that I was staying round one of the girl's houses and that I may as well sleep over rather than make the journey back. That way I could borrow one of the girl's make up and sometimes one of their evening dresses. I enjoyed it better than staying in, but I used to drink too much in order to boost my confidence and then I started smoking because I relaxed even more then with the cigarettes and it worried me really. I noticed some of the others didn't drink or smoke and they still looked happy and could talk to the others. But me, well it was like I'd drink the lager and try and join in the laughter as if it was funny. I could always hear myself laughing as if from the outside and I always thought how stupid and hollow I sounded. And no matter how much lager I drunk I'd never feel a part of them. Never. I'd always feel different. Set apart, and not, quite fitting in, and I hated it. Why was I like that, why was I so stupid and boring. Why couldn't I be like others?

It was one night in a nightclub that I met him. Immediately I knew that he understood that feeling. Not that he felt it himself but sometimes had flashes of it, sometimes felt something similar.

He'd come over to me at the end of the dance and said he'd watched me all evening but had been too scared to ask for a dance. And I'd look up at him, all 6 ft of him with dark swept black hair and these Elvis Presley eyes and I'd smile back.

We'd arranged to meet next Saturday evening outside a wine bar in Richmond that we both knew. I looked forward to it, and to seeing him again, all week. And when Saturday came it was sunny all day and the evening, one of those late Indian summer evenings that come often at the end of August and at the end of all the hot weather. I remember sitting outside the old fashioned style wine-bar on those white painted garden type chairs and drinking dry white wine and laughing. David actually made me laugh; not with wild abandon, but with genuine pleasure.

I hadn't laughed for a long time and felt as if all the greyness that had hung over me for so long had lifted and vanished without me even noticing.

He was tall and so big, that you couldn't help feel protected in his company, and with his black hair and dark eyes he looked like a fifties film star. He dressed in dark suits all the time and always wore a huge gold ruby ring on the little finger of his left hand.

The red Camero sports car he drove added to his glamour and he'd drive fast down country lanes and with the weather still good and the soft top roof pulled down, it was like being in a film and he was like some kind of magic man. He made me feel as no other before him, and I gave myself to him willingly, and with gratitude and love. Until then, I had not so much as kissed a boy in earnest, but with David, as big as he was, it all came naturally.

I met David after that on a regular basis and then it increased to every other day. He always had his entourage with him, his two friends Steve and Alan. They all appeared to work together, and, work for them, was a mish mash of buying and selling and making profits and jobs that needed doing for people who had a lot of money, and deals they always seemed to be making.

I noticed they all seemed to have an awful lot of money and David was extremely generous, showering me with presents from the very beginning. Red roses and giant bottles of Chanel No. 5 delivered to my work in the afternoon or left on my doorstep for me to find in the morning. In the end, my bedroom

43

was filled with every species of cuddly toys, huge great fluffy pandas down to tiny honey coloured Winnie the Poohs, bottles of every type of expensive fragrance, and bouquets of fresh flowers.

Instead of staying around London for weekends David would insist we'd go away down to Devon and stop off at places like Monkton where we'd stay in an old castle that had been turned into a hotel. David would always take one of his friends with him and invariably it was Steve who would come with us to run errands for David and see to our general comforts. It was a two seater sports car and Steve would climb into the boot of the car and sleep all the way to Devon, or sometimes we'd hire a four seater and Steve and Alan would sit in the back while David, American baseball cap on head, would play Daddy to us all and sing coach songs all the way to our destination like a younger version of John Candy in 'Summer Rental'. I felt like the traditional gangster's moll in the movies, but David was no mobster.

David was a born family man, the sort that should have five or six children. He'd always make sure we had all the props before we drove off for our weekends away, Food hamper in the back, flasks of coffee for the journey, hats ·for everyone and loads of country and western Don Williams tapes to play while we were driving along.

I changed my job around then. I'd always been afraid to in case of losing the job I was secure in, but with David's confidence behind me and encouragement that I could do anything I applied for a job advertised in the newspapers that I never thought I could get; a trainee private detective.

I applied for the position, went for an interview and beat thirty other applicants. Rinaldi Investigations, Ealing London. Time moved on and David and I introduced each other to our parents. Mine knew that I'd been seeing him, but had never got together with his parents and been introduced formally.

44

It was Christmas 1986 when I was 22 that David and I formally announced our engagement, with David handing me the sapphire and diamond encrusted engagement ring, and making my eyes fill with tears of happiness. No more loneliness, no more pain. I had a family of my own now, or soon would have!

We planned a long engagement until David could build me a house, but in the meantime he rented one in Hayes, two streets away from my parents' house and it was decided we wouldn't live together until after we were married, although I stayed with him every weekend and bank holidays. The house itself was an old Victorian house. It had three double bedrooms, two huge downstairs rooms and a huge old kitchen.

Steve, who went out working with David on a regular basis spent so much time around there that he moved in and had one of the downstairs rooms as his own. I never realised how possible it was for someone's life to change in such a short space of time. From all the grey cloud came a burst of hot sun, that came out and stayed out. I never realised that it was possible to be surrounded by so much love.

I'd go round to David's house straight from work for tea. I always found myself eagerly seeking its outline as I made my way along the dark streets. Even seeing it from a distance would fill me with an inner warmth. Like a haven. A place where you could be yourself. A place where you were loved and could give love in return.

Sometimes David would meet me from work, but always with some sort of stupid present he'd bought for me in a garage on the way home; a stuffed cat or a beach ball. He'd collect me from work then drive me to the corner shop where we'd pick up the tea and he'd spend ages cooking it for me and bring it to me on a tray in front of the telly. The he'd sit by me, and dip his bread in my gravy and kiss me, and drink all my coke in one go or dig his teeth into a piece of meat, and have me bite the protruding bit. Sometimes I would watch him and feel sad, he was such a sweet boy, so loving and well brought up. If only he knew, knew about my past and the fact I'd spent most of my life in orphanages, would he mind? What would he think? *He wasn't a snob, but I feared telling him anything.*

I kept my past to myself and as far as he knew I was a normal girl, with normal parents. Normal and nice, just like I wanted to be. And he loved me, and I loved him.

As far as David knew I was normal in every way, until I started behaving in a way that wasn't like the girl he had come to know and love. The jealousy.

The jealousy was like some sort of hidden monster and I hadn't even known it was there. Well not really - just that time all those years ago, when Mr. Hart had dumped me back in the orphanage.

Never having a boyfriend before, since my feelings as a child and the horrible rage feeling I felt as my foster father picked up another little girl in the orphanage, I'd never felt that feeling since then. And why should I? David was mine! Why should I feel jealousy?

I was to quickly find out that the old green feeling had some how taken root again and the feeling had doubled in size and somehow grown to an uncontrollable compulsion. Suddenly, the jealousy controlled me, I didn't control the jealousy. And I soon found out how strong a hold it had on me. It was a Saturday afternoon when David first discovered this and I was sitting outside his mother's house in Chiswick when I first saw her. Jean, David's ex-girlfriend.

I suppose I hadn't given much thought to the fact that there might have been someone else before me, but that day, sitting in the car, I realised for the first time as I watched her sail past. Dark chestnut bouncing curls keeping time as they fell down her back. She had one of those dresses that nice girls' wear, Laura Ashley type floral print that fell well over her knees. She had a figure like one of those magazine models. For no real reason, I felt like I hated her.

My body went numb with a cold, pure fear when his mother told me who she was and filled me in with some of her background. Apparently, she didn't do all that well at school but had managed to get herself a job working with children, and still lived with her parents round the corner from David's mother.

"She will be coming back later, she's quite good friends with Sue, (David's sister). She will be popping in when she gets back from work."
I was filled with horror at having to meet this Jean, someone who had once been so close to David. My David.

The whole afternoon was spoilt for me, as my stomach churned and I fought off the urge to cry or panic or stomp around as a strange anger reared up inside me, a rage that I struggled against and tried desperately to keep down. We were all seated round the tea table when she finally showed up.

My eyes were like a spotlight on David. What would his reaction be? To my relief, he paid little or no attention to her, and his indifference didn't appear to be some sort of act because of my presence. When I trusted him finally enough to take my eyes off him I turned in my seat to see her properly for the first time. A face, not exceptionally pretty certainly not ugly looked back at me. She spoke for the first time and her voice wasn't like something out of this world either. She was just average and very girl next-door. But to me she looked beautiful, my mind had become something I had little or no control over and it was throwing up pictures of her and David together, the perfect couple running along together hand in hand across a cornfield. Hopelessly in love. He'd go back to her in the end, I knew it, and I was just a temporary gap filler. I felt filled with rage and a deep bewildering sense of injustice. Why, why, was he doing this to me? Suddenly, surrounded by all those people, I was alone once again.

I sat there trembling with rage and answering any attempt at conversation that came my way with monosyllabic answers, squeezed out in a dull snappy tone.

The dinner seemed to last for ages, and even more time seemed to drag before I managed to get David alone in the car with me. Then I exploded!

"How fucking dare you? How fucking dare you? You first class bastard, belittling me in front of that ... that ... fucking tramp."

I sat very straight and stiff next to him, in the front seat, face forward and trembling with rage.

He looked at me in surprise, the usually fat jolly face temporarily without it's sparkle.

I turned to him and felt full of love as I saw his sad sweet childlike expression. It wasn't enough, I wanted to hurt him, hurt him like I was hurting. "We're finished. I've decided we're finished. I didn't love you anyway. Anyway, all the time I never loved you, there's only one person I'll ever love." It worked! His face was full of pain. I'd hurt him, but not quite enough. "I was using you; just using you all the time for all your presents and the things you bought me." I went on and on, only pausing to watch his face to see if I was hitting the target, demanding some kind of reaction. He sat there just looking at me, face like a sad, beaten puppy. When I had finished, I demanded he drive me to his house, where I slept in the spare bedroom. Then I ignored him and didn't speak to him for a week, saying I wanted to end it. And when he asked what he'd done and who it was I loved, if it wasn't him, and if I intended to go off with the man, I ignored him again and gave him no answer. The weeks dragged by and eventually we got back together again. The previously happy and fun filled relationship had vanished, and in its place came a sour, suspicious, emotional battlefield. The first display was only a beginning for the behaviour that was to become the norm in our now failing relationship.

My jealousy and possessiveness would invade everything whether it was watching a film with a beautiful girl in it, or sitting quietly in a pub where I'd accuse him of gazing over at whichever female happened to be in there at the same time.

I was terrified of losing him and shut down all my barriers and recoiled back even further into myself. Alone. Always alone ...

And yet there was so much feeling inside me, so much love to give and yet I was too scared to give it, and I couldn't understand why.

So many nights spent waiting for him to call, so many evenings where I'd let myself into his house when he said he'd be in early; watching the clock, waiting for him and watching endless television, smoking, cursing, panicking until I could burst.

Then, when he did come in he'd ignore me except for a fleeting and absent minded kiss on the cheek, have a bath, then fall straight off to sleep. I'd never felt so lost and desolate before. The contrast between the warmth of his devotion and love and the withdrawal of his attention was more that I could bear. I had destroyed everything that was good in my life.

I had succeeded in making him reject me. Now he would go back to her anyway or find someone better than me. I had just served to delay something that was inevitable anyway.

And yet we were still engaged, and he hadn't asked for the ring back. It was only later when he found out about him did he seek its return.

It was one day when he went to my handbag for something, I think it was some change; and that's when he saw the unposted letter addressed to Ian Brady. He couldn't believe it at first. He pulled it out and looked at it, then looked at me.

"That's the Moors Murderer, isn't it?" he asked incredulously. "What are you doing? . . . . I know him" I said as casually as possible. He couldn't believe it - he stood , in amazement - his face showed lines of anguish.

He couldn't take it in . . . any of it.

So I explained to him that I'd been writing to Ian Brady for a while. He didn't understand. "Do you think you're going to kill someone?."

I tried to end the conversation, "Look he won't write back to me, so it's okay."

It wasn't enough for David. "No it's not okay, what would people think of you if they found out you were writing to him? What about the parents of the children he murdered?"

I didn't count on what he'd do next, he stood up slowly. "Look, I have to think all this over. You have to go. I want to be alone. It seems to me that you keep everything to yourself, you never give anything of yourself to someone, you never give love and I don't think you're capable of it. I think you're cold. That's why you're writing to him, he's cold. You're both cold bastards together, no wonder you think you're alike, you are alike". I got up, went for my bag and made for the front door. He ran after me and stood at his front door as he shouted after me. In the dark I couldn't see his face properly, but I heard the words, and I never forgot them. "It's off, I don't want to marry you." I stopped and turned.

"Give me back the ring" he said slowly.

I took it off slowly and handed it back to him, deliberately, my eyes glazed and tearful, never leaving his, of incredulity.
"Look" he said, holding the ring in his hand, "If you stop writing these letters to him, I'll think about giving you this back."

"He's all I've got", I sobbed, "All that I ever had, he's always been there."

"Don't be stupid, you've got your home and your family, what do you mean all you've got? He killed people for God's sake, who do you think he is; a bloody saint? He means nothing. He didn't want you, doesn't want you - You don't need him!"

"I need him" I shouted back "You'll go away, you'll look at others, you'll go away, you'll stop loving me ...

. . . He will always be there" I screamed at him! Always, always. Like he always was. I ran.

David shouted after me, and his words rang in my ears, "He doesn't even know you're doing this. He doesn't know you, doesn't even know you exist, and if he does, he don't bloody want you!"

Love was dangerous, and I made up my mind never to feel it again. Only him, he was all I needed, always there in my head.
And yet David's words ring uncomfortably true, "He doesn't even want you."

A fantasy is a fantasy and I should have left it where it belonged. But you see it grew and grew until there wasn't any room for it left inside my head. It had to come out into reality. I felt too much and too strong and my feelings too real to have hidden away.

The thought of him acted like a kind of barrier from the pain of the earlier years, something solid, something to lean on.

The relationships I had with friends and with David frightened me. The sense of fear that accompanied those relationships was so great, that the friendships had virtually no chance of a successful conclusion.

51

Always and throughout the time I was with them these friends, lovers, call them what you will and as my love for them grew, along with it would come an even greater feeling; the feeling that I would lose them or they would go away or one day they would decide they didn't love me anymore, just out of the blue.

The love inside me, just too scared to go anywhere, after David, stayed inside me, and longed with a burning need to express itself and to give itself. It was like being shut away in a prison of my own creation.

I wanted someone to love and 'he' had been there. There, in my mind, like a rock, something steady. Something to hook on to, something stable in my life. It was safe to think loving thoughts about a rock, it wouldn't slip or move away, or even come to life and hurt you.

Safe to think loving thoughts about the man in the picture. He wasn't real, he was a fantasy and fantasies never hurt you.

My favourite dream, and I'd dream on some nights of a saviour, a dark haired rider on a jet black horse would carry me away to a castle on a hill surrounded by woods and away from people. He would love me more than the world. No others to come between us, just me and the rider of the dark horse. Together always.

One mind, Two bodies. Linked forever.

You can't retreat into dreams to protect you from hurt in reality. But it seems then I did. And my life started to go in a direction that had I've seen the future, I would never have steered it that way, but back then, it felt good. It felt good loving someone. And it was safe. So safe to love a man in my dream. And the feeling, the feeling of love flowing through me, unchecked, and unafraid for another person, that I began to live nearly totally within my mind, which was where he permanently dwelt . . .

When I lay alone in the darkness,
I think of you,
I am not alone,
I reach and can almost touch you,
I am not afraid,
You are always there,
You come when I call,
Warm wanting protecting,
In the darkness
I cannot see,
But I know you are there,
Loving me.

But this was no dark knight, in a dream, no person I'd made up. He was real. He was real and he was Ian Brady, a mass murderer locked away for ever. Cold and evil and incapable of love and I couldn't even reach him with my letters. - And was, in my mind but not yet proven beyond doubt, my father ... I needed to know - for once and for all, I had to be sure.

So surely it was safe - It would have been safe if I had left it at that, but I couldn't live so much inside my head. I wanted it to be real. Wanted it. And yet it was stupid, dangerous even considering who he was. And what about the murders, shouldn't I consider them? I pushed it all out of my mind.

I wanted him to know I was real and to ensure he was real, too.

1987

Dear Mr Brady,
You don't know me, but I know you from reading about you and your picture. My letters haven't been getting through whilst I wrote to you at Wormwood Scrubs but now you're in

53

Gartree I hope my letters will get to you.
I am 23 years old and work as a private detective ....
and on and on

I received no answer.

Then another.

Dear Mr Brady,

I'm sorry to bother you again but did you receive my last letter?

I got a reply. Again from the governor of Gartree prison.

Dear Miss Hart, Thank you for your letters, (Bloody hell, I thought, I hadn't written them to him) but we regret to inform you that as you had no knowledge of Mr Brady prior to his sentencing ... blah, blah, blah ...
Great, the same as before.

I tried a letter to his mentor, the peer, Lord Longford.
Dear Lord Longford,
Would it be possible perhaps for you to pass on a letter to Ian Brady? I would like to correspond with him, and maybe it would be nice for him to write to people outside.

I got a reply.

Dear Miss Hart,

I had a visit with Ian Brady a few weeks ago, during that time he was unable to speak and he is so highly disturbed I feel that there is no point in your writing. Myra Hindley however would welcome a letter and would be grateful for your support to secure her parole ...

I put the letter in the bin.

I tried again, a request to the governor of Gartree Prison Leicester, then again straight to Ian Brady.
The letters were going unanswered. There was another way.

My first holiday off work and I headed straight for the M1, North, where I stood, waiting for a lift. One of those huge ten ton lorries began to slow down, then pulled over, I climbed up into the huge cabin. "Where you headed love?" he had a northern accent. I was in luck, he was going through Manchester.

The large lorry driver was quiet most of the journey and I was left with my own thoughts. The radio played an old Neil Diamond tune as the huge truck rolled into Manchester three hours later and I looked around at the old northern buildings and the grey dusty coloured streets.

Everything seemed old and old fashioned and it seemed like I had gone back in time.
He dropped me off at Manchester, Piccadilly Station and nodded at me, then heaved the truck round and went off on his way. I headed straight for the bar and downed a martini and lemonade, and then another in quick succession.

I felt nervous and I didn't know why. I half wondered what I was doing and yet I felt so compelled to do it, that I ceased to give reason any thought.

I had a camera with me and a copy of Beyond Belief by Emlyn Williams a book about The Moors Murders. I needed it for reference purposes and the names of the roads.

Right, which way to Hattersley, I asked the nearest policeman, then blushed guiltily as he peered down at me. I was thinking it was written all over my face my reasons for going there. My copy of Beyond Belief was jutting out of my handbag and I covered it over quickly.

I had to get another train. The young policeman beamed at me as he told me how to get there.

'Did he know', I thought to myself as I made my way to the push and pull at the side of the station to get the local train to Hattersley.

The train stopped there soon enough. It was a tiny little station, and the sign hung there in black writing on white 'Hattersley'. So he was real then, or the place was.

The story I'd read about him always seemed so unreal, I couldn't believe half of it, and with the letters unanswered I began to doubt the existence of the man in the picture at all. But here it was, and here I was.

It was snowing at the time, but it stopped as soon as I made my way out of the station and down the long sloping road.
The snow was about three inches thick beneath my feet, and I had to trudge along in it. Crunch, crunch, and I crunched past a phone box ruminating on the fact that I had no friend to phone to tell where I was. I saw a pub, over on the right hand side.

I ordered a martini and lemonade and drunk it quickly. The drinks were half the normal price in London so I ordered another and sat back in the corner alone and looked at the locals. They seemed to be mostly young people and I quickly finished the drink, pulled my coat on again and walked down further. I don't know why I was walking in that particular direction, it just seemed natural. And then I saw it 'Wardle Brook Avenue' to the right. So there it was, there, where he lived. The house where he had lived and so many had died. Even a young boy hacked to death with an axe. Not real. Surely, not real. Not him. The book must have lied. Just a story, just a horror story.

I walked down Wardle Brook Avenue. Having read and re-read the book in the children's home it seemed weird. It was like entering into a dream.

A white Rover cruised slowly past me and round the corner at the end of the road then round to a small pub across the small patch of green. Two ladies, gossiping came round the far corner, stopped chattering, when they saw me, a stranger. I could see the name of the pub by now.

The New Inn.

It was a small country style pub, and I followed the direction the car had taken and walked along the sparsely housed road towards it.

That's when I looked over and saw it, the house, it was like all other houses, No. 16. Just sitting there; Existing. Sitting back in the dark and covered in snow.
As I came up to the pub doorway, I noticed that it was lined by five or so young men, all standing there, pints in hands watching me.

"You're not thinking of coming in here are you?" One of them asked. "Yes" I said timidly. I'd heard the locals were funny about people coming up and looking at the house and area because of the murders, but this was ridiculous. They couldn't stop me from going in the pub. I pushed past them and then turned in surprise to see them follow me inside, then circle me at the bar.

I felt scared, and lies about visiting an aunt who lived in the area were forming in my mind.

57

"Are you a model? My mates are all in love with you" one of them said in the flat Manchester accent.

I breathed a sign of relief.

"Are you German or Swedish"?

I smiled back at them. "No, I'm English."

I ordered a drink, turned down their offer of paying for it and went and sat down. With that two of them came and sat either side of me. I'd heard about Northerners being friendly, but I didn't realise they were that friendly. By that time, I'd had enough to drink to make me relax and to be at my creative best. Various lies were bubbling up in my head. I chose one of them and recited it. I was a journalist from Woman's Own Magazine doing a story on Ian Brady and I'd lost my photographer at Manchester Piccadilly.

The big guy who owned the white Rover asked me had I seen the house. When I said no, he offered to take me over the road to see it. I finished my drink, and we made our way over there . . .

It seemed like any other council house, No. 16. A white gate and a small front garden. About ten or so young children on push bikes surrounded the house and stared at me as I pushed past them up to the front door.

It was covered over by another false front door and bolted down. The windows as well, all had false fronts and were securely bolted down. It was to keep the young children out who habitually tried to get inside and dare each other to sleep there overnight. I hurried round and wondered where the man with the white Rover had gone. I walked up the front path and looked down the road and there he was, about half a mile up the road.

"I'm not going near it" he shouted up to me. He stood there, fat with his round big frightened eyes staring in horror, and I couldn't help but laugh as I went to join him.

"I don't care what you say, it's evil spirits, demons and things like that. The dead children were buried on the Moors in a semi-circle, not many people know that, it's evil."

"There's nothing supernatural about murder, is there"? I said, and looked at him curiously. In the end we drove to Glossop to try and find me somewhere to stay the night. I booked into a bed and breakfast there called The Red Lion and went for a drink with him.
We sat there sipping beer and he started talking to me about the effect the murders had had on the whole of the Manchester area.

"That's all anyone ever talks about" he told me. It's like it was the most unrealist thing that has ever happened round here, all that ever happens is everyday life. It's a mystery you see to people, they want to know why he did it. There doesn't seem to have been a reason, and none of the experts have been able to explain it, I mean, they were like killed in the horriblest way. He's either really evil or he's mad."

Neither of our theories was coming to much, and with the effect of the alcohol, I considered confiding to him what I was doing there, how I was feeling . . . who I was.

How I felt, guilty, stupid and troubled.

Guilty as if I had done all the killing. This was his past, the man in the picture, not mine. What was I trying to involve myself for?

I sat there debating whether to tell him what I was thinking, and thought about the fact that human beings never really do make contact. Our most profound

59

thoughts are never spoken aloud. It would not be socially acceptable. Only small talk is. We kept our deepest thoughts to ourselves. We were all really tiny islands. No-one really knew anyone else. We were all alone. Alone within our own heads.

I was thinking about all this, when I realised that he was talking to me.

"Well I have to go now, I'm on night shift at the bakery, sleep well won't you." He went.

And all of a sudden I felt incredibly alone.

I had a good night's sleep and in the morning I walked around the tiny Glossop village and got a film for my camera.

I had quite a bad hangover from the steady drinking I'd done the night before and the sun was out, watery, but bright enough to dazzle me as it reflected off the snow, and made my head pound even more.
I got a taxi, all the way back to Wardle Brook Avenue and walked up the road towards the house.
I walked up the front path and began to shake at the front door to try and loosen the bolts on the covering door. I got really carried away pulling on it. I was just getting somewhere when the door burst open and a tall dark haired man stood watching me from inside.

I gasped in fright and jumped back.

"What are you doing?" he asked abruptly, with that strange flat vowelled accent.

"I'm a reporter from Woman's Own, I'm taking some pictures of the house for a story I have to do. Mind if I come in"? He stood in the doorway, "No, I'm only based here with the council handling the heating enquiries for the estate. It's more than my job's worth to let you in."

I could see in the house as he stood blocking the doorway, stark white walls and pale grey carpet. The staircase stood tall and narrow to the left side of the front door and three separate doors faced you as you as you went in. The furthest was open. The kitchen.

I moved back and he shut the door.

I stood over near the gate and started clicking. I re-filled the camera after 25 shots then went round the back and took another 25. Every angle of view of the back of the house and every angle of view from the front, including the view over to the'New Inn' right up to the rolling Lancashire hills to Derbyshire's National Park area beyond.

A neighbour shouted over, "Are you doing that for your own pleasure?."

I moved away from the house and doubled back along the side of the house and the small alleyway that ran through the back and down Pudding Lane and along to Underwood Court.

I stood in front of the block of flats then pointed the camera upwards towards the third floor and then clicked away again with my camera.

I got the train back to London from Manchester Piccadilly. In the coffee bar on the buffet carriage on the train I saw it in the newspaper I had picked up and was browsing through. Ian Brady, Moors Murderer, moved to Park Lane Top Security Prison for the criminally insane.

Then when I got back to London I got the photos printed up and sent one of them off with a letter, "I've got more of these which I'll send if you like", and posted the letter; addressee Ian Brady, Park Lane Liverpool.

I was working around then for a new firm, Worldwide Investigations in Hammersmith, West London. It was April 1987 and the beginning of a beautiful summer. I was twenty three that year. I was still living at home in Hayes with my foster parents and David still lived round the corner. We were no longer boyfriend and girlfriend but we had become friends and I saw him almost on a daily basis.

I had taken driving lessons and I'd even passed my test and bought myself a second hand car, a bright red Austin Allegro.

That summer was beautiful, it was only April and only the beginning but you could tell that it was going to be hot that year, one of those summers where you could fry eggs on the pavement.

I felt excited all that month, I felt as if something was in the air, something good or something crazy was about to happen.

The first strange thing to happen was Alan phoning. Alan Taylor who I'd worked with at Rinaldi Investigations. It was a while since I'd heard from him and the phone call was out of the blue, while I was at the office one afternoon. I thought he'd probably be phoning to arrange a date and I remember feeling pleased. I hadn't seen him for about a year and David was the only friend I had, so it would have been nice to see someone else for a change.

Straight away and even though I had not seen him for a year, Alan started telling me about this psychic.

"Loads of people I know have seen him, he's called Mike Baker and his offices are in Holborn."

I was surprised and disinterested. Alan and I had been great friends at Rinaldis and we regularly got together for a drink. As he hadn't phoned and we hadn't seen each other for quite a while, I thought he'd want to arrange to meet up.

"Oh no, sorry, I can't make it for a drink. Look, you must go to this psychic, I'll ring for you and make an appointment."

"But I don't need a psychic, much less believe in them, and I don't even know anyone who's dead."

"Yes, but they know you", he enthused.

I don't know why I let him talk me into it. It was different I suppose and I was bored, and I looked forward to meeting him for a drink afterwards to talk and laugh about it and talk over old times. Later on that day I found myself phoning Mike Baker the clairvoyant and arranging for an evening after work that week.

I put down the phone and wondered why the hell I had done that. I didn't even believe in psychics. I thought the whole thing was rubbish and I didn't even want to know anything about dead people. Once you were dead you were dead that was it.

It was with a cynical mind that I got on the train that Wednesday evening, and headed in the opposite direction to my usual way home.

When I arrived at the address the receptionist had given over the phone, I found an office type building and on the third floor what looked like an accountants or a solicitors.

The receptionist was just about to leave, "Oh, you must be Christine; go straight in, Mike's expecting you."

I walked into the rather small office behind her. A middle aged grey haired man stood up from behind a desk hand outstretched. "Christine, glad you could make it." The receptionist had quoted 30 pounds for an hour over the phone, and I had three ten pound notes curled up in my hand ready for the moment when I'd have to hand it over to him.

He indicated to me to sit down, then walked round the desk and shut the door. He had one of those West Country accents from Devon or somewhere like that, and you couldn't help but relax in his company.

My mind was fixed in a state of total disbelief and I eyed him cynically.

Then as if he somehow knew what I was thinking, he leaned forward and began, "Right; Before I begin, I want you to drop your air of cynicism, if you don't believe in communication with the dead, and that the future is already written, and some are able to read it for you, then that is up to you, but you are here, and you are going to pay for my services, so rather than waste your money I suggest you keep an open mind."

I squirmed in my seat like an errant kid in front of the headmaster.

"Now I'll start" he said softly as he leaned back, shut his eyes and started to talk. "I see acting, acting, a very strong feeling of that, but never mind it's not something you're supposed to go into but maybe a previous life, I'm not sure."

"A previous life" I said in amazement, a smile of amusement on my lips.

He opened his eyes and looked at me. "I must ask you not to interrupt. Now I see you in a job, a job that you are in now, but won't be in for long. Think of it as temporary. By the end of the year, let's say before October you will be out of the country, somewhere hot, somewhere like Greece, then you'll return to London, and then you'll go again, this time to America. America is the place for you."

I thought of the amount of money I had in the building society, and wondered how I was going to finance leaving my job and jet setting it around the World and sat there with the thirty pounds wet and hot in my fist and thinking of all the other things that I could have bought with it.

"You will go backwards and forwards from America to London, but your base will be in this country. And whatever you decide to do, whatever it is, you will be successful, You are a girl who is looking for something, some sort of answer, to some question, well keep looking, keep going because you will find it in the end."

I looked at the clock on the wall behind him. Half an hour had gone past, and I felt relieved, only another half an hour to go, what he was saying was annoying me, it was all so unbelievable, I would never leave my job, I loved it there, and as for going to Greece, or somewhere hot, then America, well I hated hot countries, and I had wanted to go to America, but I'd always been too scared, I couldn't pack up and leave this country and go and live somewhere where I didn't know anyone, I'd miss David too much anyway.

I hadn't heard it all yet. The best was to come.
"You'll make contact with the media" Mike went on, "Then once contact is made it will never be broken, and there will be someone called P who you will think is the one for you, but he's not, J is. J is the only one who can make you happy. This J is your soul mate, he is you, you understand, and you will marry him by early next year, then that'll be it, no-one else for either of you, you will meet him, I think near a birthday, someone in your family's birthday. That is if you haven't met him already. I can also see an old boyfriend coming back into your life P or R, does that make sense?."

I looked at him blandly, none of it made sense.

He opened his eyes and directed a steady gaze towards me, "Now", he started,

"I'm going to let you address a question yourself, straight to my guide, what I want you to do is to say the question in thought form in your head, then my guide will tell me the answer and I will recite it to you."

I thought the whole thing ridiculous, but I thought I may as well think something. I closed my eyes and thought deeply. Okay what was it I wanted to know, that no-one could ever tell me, I know, and I thought the question, 'What's the link between myself and Ian Brady?'

Mike paused for a while then appeared to be listening, until suddenly he looked at me, "In a week, does that make sense?."

I looked at him coldly, it didn't make sense at all, I stood up, "The hour's up isn't it?"

Coming out of there I remember I saw a tramp who stopped me and asked me for a couple of pence for a cup of tea. After spending 30 pounds for an hour of rubbish I was raging with anger, "Sod Alan", I'd been better off handing it all to the tramp. And now I hadn't even got ten pence more than my train fare home.

I cast the tramp a sympathetic glance and apologised as I hurried on past him.

I mean it was all such a load of rubbish, I mean P and J and success. I remember in work I sat next to a boy called Paul who was always travelling and across the desk was someone called John, who always wanted to go to the States. I remember telling the receptionist Gillian at work and her creasing up with laughter and saying, "So you're going to be the office slut, first Paul then John then you'll probably end up on page three of the Sun, that's what he meant by contact with the media." She was a West Indian girl and her teeth shone out whiter than white and she rocked to and fro on her chair with mirth.

Alan phoned later on that day and when he still said he couldn't make it for a drink I was a bit short with him. The wages I was on at the time were quite low as I was still training and the thirty pounds had made quite a dent in them.

Time passed and I forgot all about the psychic except for David's sarcastic remarks about whether or not I had my suitcase packed for my big holidays in Greece and America.

I would have ignored all the psychic had said as rubbish but one thing came right and almost straight away.

'What's the connection between me and Ian Brady?'
One week, he'd said and I hardened against him.

One week. One week. What does that mean? That was no answer!

I didn't know it but the fantasy was just about to become a reality. The following Wednesday, exactly a week after I'd visited Mike Baker something came in the post.

I didn't notice it first, a long brown envelope with long sloping handwriting on the front in blue biro.

It looked official, I glanced at it when I came in late Wednesday evening, then ignored it and decided to read it in the morning.

I remember I woke up that morning and I went downstairs as usual, and made a cup of tea and some toast, and bought it back upstairs with me. I stopped on the stairs and popped the letter between my teeth and carried on up back to bed.

I remember thinking that it might be from a doctor at Park Lane after seeing the Liverpool postmark; probably telling me I couldn't write to him. I peeled it open expecting the usual.

I think when I did pull out the white sheet of paper I don't think it registered at first. It was all this writing in blue biro and the first thing I did was glance at the name on the bottom. There was a signature and it said ... Best Wishes ... Ian! ...

I thought, no, this is some sort of joke, not after all these years. I felt funny, weird like, I was going to cry or something and excited; like it was like something magic or something.

I mean all that wanting, all that time. All those years ago, when he'd been just someone in a picture, someone I thought was dead, and now not only was he alive, he was writing to me. He knew I existed, he'd put my name there at the top.

I don't think I've ever felt as good as I did that day. It was like it wasn't futile and pointless and grey any more. Life had meaning and truth and the world was an exciting place where anything could happen, where dreams, come true and strange things happened.

I felt that I was Alice and I had just slipped through the looking glass and everything had turned into a fantasy, and it was real, more real than all of it. I could feel it and it was more intense, more full of life than any feeling that I had ever had previously.
He was mine. All mine, now nothing would come in the way of that. Nothing would come in the way of me and him having each other and no-one else coming in the way of that.
I don't think I even read the letter, until hours later. It didn't matter to me what it said just that he knew that I existed. That was all that mattered. I tried David's phone number; there was no answer. I dialled it again, still no answer. I had to tell someone, I felt I was going to burst.

Doug my social worker was the next one I tried, he agreed to meet me in half an hour in the Music Box, the pub around the corner from me.

He was surprised at the change in me.

"You look well" he said, as he bought two halves of lager and brought them over to us in the table in the corner of the pub.

"No work today? I thought you were the big career girl with the car and working towards promotion."

"Yes, I am, but I had to take today off, today's a magic day, today's a day when anything can happen."
He looked at me, and sipped his beer slowly, a residue of foam sticking to the moustache on his top lip.

"Oh Doug, you know all that time before the overdose, all that time in Olympic I only kept going because of him, and I knew he was like me, we're so alike, you see I knew one day we would be like so close, I just knew it," I rambled on excitedly, "Well today it came, a letter from him, actually from him, I could hardly believe it and that's it now, for keeps, I've got someone that's mine. He'll understand me, because we're like each other, we're the same, Doug. I'm never going to be lonely again, not ever."

I didn't expect the reaction I got, "Ever since I've known you Chris, you've been on about him. I've watched you become more and more wrapped up with him, and obsessed with him. It's not real though. The person that wrote this letter is Ian Brady, who is cold and evil and a mass murderer. The man in the photo you stuck to your bed is the man in your head, and some sort of fantasy. A saviour who could come and rescue you and make all the pain go away. The father figure that you craved. The two aren't the same. You've done it now, anyway, you've succeeded in getting a letter from him. Now leave it!"

I couldn't believe my ears. I thought he'd be pleased for me.

"Leave it, you are kidding aren't you? This is just the start."

I started getting over excited, egged on by the lager I was knocking back.

"Look why do you have to do this? You're not an unlovable person, you've just had bad luck. Why are you trying to obtain something off someone so out of reach both physically and mentally? You can't possibly hope to get anything back from him, he's been in prison for a long time and in solitary confinement for nearly twenty years, he'll be disturbed and Christine, you're disturbed too. What sort of relationship could you possibly have, what could you do for each other, care for each other like father and daughter?"

I got angry, "I'm not disturbed as you put it, who's kept a job down now for three years? There's nothing wrong with me, I invited you here as a friend, not as a social worker."

He reached over and grabbed my hand and looked at me intensely, "I'm telling you you will get hurt, in some sort of way, you will get hurt."

I got up, "I'm going Doug, you're spoiling my day."

He looked up at me, and I walked out. I'd been happy before I'd seen him and now he'd made everything grey.

Not reply to Ian? He had to be kidding!

I made my way round to David's house, he was in this time. Curtains drawn and slobbing in bed. I seated myself in his huge armchair at the end of his bed and sat there waiting to get his attention. A great big bulge underneath the royal blue duvet moved and David's face peered over the top, bleary eyed, face soft and puffy covered in creases where he'd slept face down into the pillow.

"I tried you earlier" I burst out agitated and clutching the letter, I could hardly wait to tell him.

"Yes, I heard the phone, I was asleep, I was up all last night watching videos." His head sank back down on the pillow.

"Guess what", I half shouted at him, "I've only got a letter from Ian Brady." I brandished it at him and he leant over and snatched it off me and looked at it, he spent about three minutes looking at it then threw it back at me.
"No wonder you've got no friends" he started, humourously cynical, the way he always did, "Waking people up then waving letters from mass murderers at them."

I sat back in the chair, a smug smile on my face, "Aren't you pleased for me?"

"If you didn't write it to yourself, I suppose I am, if that is your burning ambition in life, which I know it is."
I ignored his sarcasm and folded the letter back into the envelope.

Later that evening while alone in my bedroom I read his letter.

> *"Yes, I would be interested in any photos you have. The one you sent of the house bought back many memories, some good some bad. So you went up to Hattersley, I find that very interesting, you must have got some strange looks if you were taking photos - I'm sorry I took so long in replying, I haven't been too well lately. Again thank you for your letter and the photo.*
>
> *Best Wishes, Ian.*

I didn't really know what to reply.

I think I put, "I'm sending you the rest of the photos, there is over a hundred in all, so I'll send them in batches. I took some of where you used to work in

Millwards, or should I say the area where it was, it was knocked down years ago, did you know?"

The reply came within ten days or so, "I was surprised to hear Millwards had been knocked down."

It was strange talking to him, I think I wanted all at once to be, like great friends, but I learned very quickly that he didn't like to be familiar too soon. And his letters although frequent coming after that on a weekly basis, he was quite cold really, quite hard to break into, like he seemed to keep it all in, keep himself in or a part of himself like Ray had told me I'd done. But this was real, and he was real, and I'd have to get to know him, the real him. I'd have to chip through the ice, and I'd have to take it slowly.

(Some letters from Ian Brady are reproduced later in this biography).

I dragged the fantasy into the reality. And maybe fantasies should stay where they belong.

I saw it as a chance though, a chance to bring him happiness and a chance to give him strength like he had given strength to me, during those long and empty years of my childhood. The man in the picture had come to life and now nothing bad could possibly ever happen.

It's hard to draw a line between fantasy and reality, because one is in the mind and the other in matter, but aren't they both linked anyway?

I didn't bother to say to myself, that I didn't know him and that it was crazy to think I cared about him and what about his crimes and the fact he was so infamous. I just put all thought of that out of my head and wrote to him on a weekly basis as if he were my personal and private friend, as in my mind he really was.

72

It was April the 17th 1987, when I got that first letter, and I remember that summer for being well and truly devoted to him. His letters were still rather prickly and cold, but he'd change I told myself, and kept ploughing on. I'd been stuck at first for what to say and I remember saying stupid things like 'do you really like the Harry Lime Theme? like they say in Beyond Belief, and asking him what books he read and talking about Nietzsche with him. I imagined that that is what he wrote about to everyone, literature, he liked books and you could tell that he knew a lot about them. He'd read a lot of Russian literature, and encouraged me to read Dostoevsky. I read Crime and Punishment and argued with him that Raskilinov was a weakling and not strong at all, and my view was the same as Judd Steiners in the book 'Compulsion'. Another book I'd read and he'd read, years ago.

I had a long correspondence with him about books, and I started to order long lists from the library so I could keep up with him, but strangely, I had already read many of them, even those that were quite bizarre and made strange companions.

I was up half the night strolling through 'The rise and Fall of The Third Reich' when I discovered he wasn't interested in that sort of thing any more but now had stringent left wing political beliefs. The numerous books I'd been reading, on the occult, a subject that had never interested me but that I had heard he was interested in, also didn't interest him.

I became at a loss to know what to talk to him about, he was fifty years of age, I was twenty three and although our backgrounds were incredibly alike, there seemed to be no meeting ground between us, and the great close friendship I had envisaged, didn't seem to be happening. I slammed shut the books I was up all night studying. It wasn't working. Yet there seemed to be something strong drawing us together.

These books that I was reading, were totally the wrong choice. Oh yes, he'd read them, but he'd read them when he was my age, before the crimes, the murders and before life imprisonment. The occult books frightened me, I'd never dared go near them in the library before, and now I was consuming them without a second thought and learning about things I hadn't wanted to even acknowledge existed.

Our letters to each other went backwards and forwards until I had a whole stack of them shoved into a shoe box underneath my bed. I even asked David his advice for what to write. "I'll compose replies then, and you copy them out in your handwriting" he offered, "No, no," I interrupted, "Myra Hindley did that when she couldn't think of what to say to him, it's not fair, not fair on him. Mind you, I can see her point, she said that there's a part of him she couldn't quite touch, couldn't penetrate. And that's true, he keeps himself to himself, I mean the very core of him and that's the part I wanted."

"Well if his girlfriend at the time of the murders couldn't get near to him, you'll never be able to."

"But that's just it", I snapped, "She said she never felt like him, she didn't feel different and not belonging as he did, so she wasn't the same kind."
"And you are I suppose? Ray said derisively.

"Yes, I am, I've always been" I said impassibly.
"Well then, why do you get letters like everyone else gets, long letters on something like Russian literature but short notes when he can't be bothered."

I looked at him angrily, but he was right. No-one seemed to break through this guard that he had. Myra Hindley hadn't been able to, nor had writers that had written about him, policemen who had visited him about further murders. To everyone he had remained 'an enigma'. He was a man who lived within and held his secrets close to his chest. No-one could touch him.

And having a relationship with him was like skating on thin ice - he was slow to open up and quick to offend. I persevered, and just kept writing whatever came into my head.

'Epic letters is all I can say about them' Ian commented in one of his replies. They were twenty and thirty page long letters where I'd cut out bits from books and send in photos and things. Quote poetry and discuss what the meaning of everything was, something that had always obsessed me. What? How and why?

I was still working around this time but I'd take a lot of time off work and spend a lot of time with David, we'd drifted back into a boyfriend and girlfriend relationship and although the talk of marriage wasn't mentioned, I suppose we just both assumed it would take place at sometime or other. David had accepted the fact that I wrote to Ian, although he didn't like it and I think at the time felt that it was something that he had to put up with or he'd lose me.

I'd spend a lot of time round his house that summer, in his back garden in the sun, sat over endless bottles of wine, 'My philosophy is blah blah, I'd solve the meaning of the universe half cut over a few bottles of red wine.'

I still had a few other friends I'd see around then. My best friend Maya, and her boyfriend Steve, who I'd go out for drinks with about once every fortnight.

I'd met them one night in The Queen Victoria in Ealing. Maya was a very pretty girl, thin pale faced with long tumbling dark hair and a face like Debra Winger. I'd known her for about five or six years and we'd become really close. Recently she'd started going out with Steve her latest boyfriend and it annoyed me a bit that we'd grown a bit distant and not had our previous girly chats. Steve always had to be there.

We were all sitting there that one Saturday night and all of us had had quite a lot to drink, when Maya started talking about the occult. She'd always been interested in it and had lent me the two books that I had on the subject at home.

"You've never been interested in it before, why now?" she asked.
I was aware that she hadn't told Steve about me writing to Ian, she'd said that he wouldn't have approved so I agreed not to mention it.

"It's him you know", I said trying to avoid his name, "He read it all when he was my age, so I thought it would prove a talking point, but I don't think he's interested any more because he didn't mention it in any replies."
'You want to watch it", said Maya amused, "Your sort shouldn't go knocking on doors in case they're answered."

"What do you mean?"I asked.

"I dunno, I just read that a particular sort shouldn't. It's rubbish though, I've been studying it for years and I've never had any results for my work."

"What are you two going on about?" butted in Steve, who had previously been sitting there absorbed in his pint of beer.
I don't know whether it was because of the drink inside me but I decided as I nearly always did that I wanted to talk about Ian, so I turned to Steve and broached the subject.

The reaction was immediate.

"He should have been hung, that bastard" he intoned in a voice full of hate.
I felt an inner revulsion, as I did towards anyone who expressed that view towards someone they knew only by newspaper reports and books written by writers who had made the whole thing up and had never even met him.

He didn't know Ian Brady or anyone else in prison for murder for no reason. It was impossible for us to understand. None of us 'knew them'. We knew the actions which were horrifying and ugly, we did not know the people. Despise and loathe the evil and the actions but don't sit in judgement on the person. Well, not until you had the bird's eye view of God himself and could see all factors involved. We here, well we only see the surface of everything so we're not fit to judge at all.

I was sipping the half of lager in front of me and putting this to Steve, and he was sitting there and I thought he understood what I was saying, so to get over my point, I began to tell him of how I had preconceived ideas of what he'd be like and how the person I knew was quite different. Maya shot me a warning glance, and I ignored it and pulled out one of Ian's letters I hadn't replied to yet out of my handbag.

I suppose it was stupid but I didn't think before I acted which is usual, and it was out of my bag before I knew what I was doing.

Steve's previously friendly face twisted into a mask of anger, "You're writing to him, that child killer, you're writing to him after he killed all those kids, you're fucking sick." He got up and Maya stood up with him. I sat there looking up at them wide eyed, not knowing what to say - I didn't have to say anything.

I looked down, then up again and my eyes blurred with a cold sting as he flung the near full pint of beer completely over me. My hair stuck to my face, and I covered my eyes with my hands as he leaned over me with the empty glass in his hand, "I ought to stick this in your face" he said slowly. He turned and walked towards the door, about half the pub by now had turned to see what all the noise was about, and were standing around staring at me. I looked up at Maya, but she didn't look back just followed him out of the pub.

Ian's letter in front of me was drenched with beer and the neat sloping handwriting in ink pen blurred and smudged so you could hardly read it.

I never did see Maya again after that, she was only one of the few friends that I had and that I lost because they didn't want to be associated with someone who was 'connected' to Ian Brady.

I learned after a lot of other incidents like that to shut up about it. The best reactions were a cold disinterest, the worst was when they wanted to kill me.

So much hatred from young and old alike for someone whose crimes dated back twenty odd years. Still something about the murders or about Ian or his girlfriend at the time, Myra Hindley, appeared in the papers on an almost daily basis. The hatred was kept alive.

I wondered how he felt to be hated that strongly, and even by the people who guarded him and the people with whom he was incarcerated. With no further contact from Myra Hindley and completely alone. How did it feel? I asked him. Then wished I hadn't. It seemed the question of a cruel child, insensitive and deliberately spiteful. He didn't reply.

I remember once Spike Milligan appeared on television on a talk show. He was Ian's favourite and I knew he'd be watching him, so whilst writing a letter and before I'd watched the interview, I wrote "Spike Milligan was great wasn't he?" I really admire him - then later I watched it so I could talk about it to him and because I knew he too would be sitting there watching it.

This host did this interview, then at the end, Wogan or whoever it was said to him, "Now we've come to the end of the interview, is there anything you'd like to say?"

And Spike Milligan all of a sudden goes really quiet and serious after all the laughter and says in a cold deliberate way "I just want to say I can't bear the scum that kill children and they should all be hung." And it was like so out of the blue, as if it was purposely directed at Ian. And I kind of felt for him. I felt a sinking feeling inside and a pain. I could practically see him, and see his face as he was just enjoying the show, then reminded "Hey, you're not allowed to laugh."

It hurt a bit, to think of that.

I couldn't stop that bloody letter I'd already posted. I suppose he thought I was probably trying to make some sort of point.

Anyway, the next letter I received was equally as cold as the others, so nothing had changed. He kept saying that he wanted to get better conditions for visiting - and I remember not paying much attention to it. Visiting him was something that I had never even considered. It was a well known fact that he hadn't seen anyone for nine years and even Lord Longford hadn't visited him for the last four years. I never even considered the possibility of a visit and he stressed to me in letters that he never had visits or did he intend to in the future. Then it was only a week later that I got an out of sequence letter, 'when you visit phone my Doctor, Dr Strickland, and tell him the date and time you will arrive, I look forward to seeing you."

I couldn't believe it. Visit him! I phoned up Alan from Rinaldis, straight away. He always gave me good advice and I went to him with everything.

"That's bizarre" said Alan, when I told him the news, "Read me the letter where he's asked you." I read out the letter down the phone. At the end of it Ian had said 'You quote my favourite poem, how did you know?'
"What poem did you quote?", Alan asked.

"Oh I just picked it, I didn't know it was his favourite, I just took a liking to it. 'Tiger, tiger burning bright', I recited.

Alan finished it for me 'In the forests of the night, what immortal hand or eye, could frame the fearful symmetry, in what distant depths or skies, burnt the fire of thine eyes? On what wings dare he aspire, what the hand dare seize the fire. What the hammer what the chain, In what furnace was thy brain. What the anvil, what dread grasp. Dare its deadly terrors clasp. When the stars threw down their spears, And watered heaven with their tears. Did he smile his work to see? Did he who made the lamb make thee?'

I told Alan I'd phone him again soon, and I folded the letter away. I don't think I could grasp the thing. I mean, visit him. To meet him and talk to him. What would I say? The letters had been hard enough. Would he be horrible? Would he be like all the books and newspapers said?

In my mind he wasn't real, he was a fantasy, he'd been the man in the picture over my bed; all those nights in the orphanage.
He wasn't real

Writing to him was strange enough and yet I could pretend the letters were going off somewhere miles away; it was still a fantasy. To meet him. Actually meet him. And was he real anyway? I couldn't separate fantasy from reality, the man in the picture from Ian Brady, the Moors Murderer, yet aren't they one and the same, and wasn't I drawn to him because he was a 'kind'? Wasn't it all meant to be for some reason, of which I knew nothing? Was blood thicker than . . . the unknown?

I'd seen people's reactions to my writing to him, yet now I was going to visit him. Then I would really become involved with him. There would be no going back, he would be real to me, and I real to him.

Maybe I wasn't thinking straight. Maybe I had just got wrapped into a silly dream, and now I was doing something evil, something wrong. He was real, and he was Ian Brady. And I was getting more and more involved. *Maybe the social worker had been kidding me - winding me up, and had thereby, created this catalyst in my head.*

I went where I have always gone as a child to make decisions, and to ask who I have always asked.

I went to the church, the old Roman Catholic Church where I had made my first holy communion and where my foster parents had brought me every

Sunday when I was a child. I walked into the old church and blessed myself from the font of Holy Water in front of the huge statue of Mary holding Jesus after he'd been taken down from the cross. I stood staring at the statue for a while, the look of anguish in the eyes of the Mother of Jesus, and Him, after being crucified for our sins, bleeding, dying, we'd done that to him by our sins and our badness when we'd turned against God and decided to go our own way. I stood there for a while looking, then opened the inner doors and walked into the church.

I looked over at the confessionals and noticed the green light was on above the confessional box, so I walked over to it and went in.

I knelt down in the small box and went automatically to say my confession like I had hundreds of times before, when I realised that that is not what I had come for. I hesitated, then went ahead. "Can I ask you something Father?" I half whispered, "Is there such a thing as evil?." There was a pause and he pulled back the curtain. I could half see him and I recognised him, Father Byrne, old and suffering from Parkinsons Disease, I remembered him from right back when I was small.

He didn't give me the answer I wanted. "Yes, there is, there is unfortunately so much evil, what is it that you are concerned with?"
I didn't know whether to tell him or not and I was so upset by what he'd said that I started to cry.

He stood up in the little box, "I've finished the confessions for today. Would you like to come and talk to me in the church hall?" I agreed and got up and waited for him to disrobe, then followed him through the church and back through the side doors to the part where the priests prepare at the back.

He sat down on an armchair opposite me and put his fingers to his lips. "You're very upset about something. Now I don't know if I can help but anything you tell me will be kept between you and I."

I wiped my face dry with the back of my hands and looked at him. Priests had always filled me with a deep sense of trust and security, men of God, pure and beautiful. I smiled at him, he'd understand, and I poured out the whole story. While I was telling it, he sat, like he did in confessional, turning sideways on to me, head leaning on one side and just listening."

"Anyway that's it," I finished "And it was okay, well sort of okay until now. I mean, before, I could control it, I didn't feel that I was doing much harm, but now, I mean, I'm going to go and visit him. I just, I wanted to get it clear", I faltered, "That I wasn't being evil, you know."

I stopped and he looked at me.

I don't think I was expecting the answer he gave, in fact I know I wasn't expecting it. I thought that he'd say to me, that it was okay. No-one was evil, and shouldn't judge anyone, we were all God's children.

Until he said it, and it was like some sort of horrible shock. "You must not visit this man, he is evil. He has chosen to stand against God, and now he is a lost soul." I wanted to shout at him "No, no you're wrong", but I just sat there and went numb and listened.

"Now you're an unusual girl", he went on. "It's not often someone of your age questions the meaning of our existence and the point of it all, in the way you seem to, and you even want to do something to help, which you can do. There's voluntary work that you can do which I will tell you about later."

I interrupted, "But they can all do that, you see I believe that there's something about me, that makes me the same type as him, so I can help him. You see I'm the only one that can help him, so I must."

He looked at me, kind soft pale blue eyes, his hands were shaking from the Parkinsons Disease and I felt a warmth towards him, kind, strong, good man, whose life had been devoted to Christ.

"He is lost", he said slowly, "You cannot help him, leave him, forget all ideas of visiting him."
I felt nauseous and cold inside like I was going to throw up and I promised the Father I wouldn't see him again, then made my way out to the front of the church.

It was all so familiar to me the smell of fresh furniture polish and the feel of the wooden benches. I knelt in front of the big altar and bowed my head. All around me there were the stations of the cross - the struggle of Jesus as he made his way to be crucified. I looked round at them and read the inscriptions. Then looked up to a huge crucifix above the altar, up there grand and powerful. I took it all in and remembered all the times I'd felt alone and lonely and how I'd come here to talk to God and tell him all my problems. God wasn't like a person, he would never let you down, and he was always there loving everyone equally.

I sat for hours that afternoon, just staring at that altar, and wondering what it would be like to live without God. I sat and thought how lonely that would be and how empty and pointless without God. I thought of Ian Brady, I thought of me telling him that I was going to stop writing to him and tell him that I wouldn't be visiting him after all, or maybe I would just not reply to his latest letter, and leave him to wait and wonder.

This all went through my head, and I looked at the giant painting above the altar: The Virgin Mary looking proud and strong. Like God - Strong.

God was strong. He didn't need me. Didn't need my love. He had so many people's love, he wouldn't miss mine.

He hadn't missed Ian's so he wouldn't miss mine. Ian needed someone. He didn't even have anyone, not even God.

I looked up at the huge crucifix. I'd brought the things in my bag.
My first Holy Communion prayer book, I'd kept my rosary beads I was given by the matron of the orphanage, pale blue and beautiful, and I'd kept them for years, and the Bible, the one that I'd always had, gold lettering and red leather bound. I tucked them all into the prayer book holder in front of where I knelt. Then got up and walked out. I turned and noticed the Father over near the holy tabernacle preparing for the evening mass. He looked over at me and smiled and nodded, "I hope you have come to some sort of decision."

"I have", I replied.

I walked towards the back doors of the church. An organist started to warm up the organ for the evening hymns and the sound of it took me back to May Processions where I'd carried baskets full of rose petals and scattered them on the ground while wearing my first Holy Communion dress.

God was on one side, Ian Brady was on the other. I couldn't have God if I was going to give my love to Ian. I cried that day, the day I said goodbye to God, I just stopped once and turned and I said it before I walked out. I mean I loved him, so much, but he seemed to me to be mean, to not be what I thought he was. And I just turned and said it just quietly and I hoped he heard. I whispered to him that I loved him, but that it was for the last time, that I was there.

I don't know whether it was that night or not, or whether now that my memory is playing tricks on me, and making it seem that everything happened at once.

But it was one night then, or very shortly after, that I lay in my bed, with the window open, blowing the curtains around and cooling the beads of sweat that had come up on my face, that in some time between sleeping and waking that I heard them, calling my name over and over, and I woke up with a start, wondering whether I was dreaming or had I been awake: And I got up and shut the window tightly, where it had been blown by the wind and had been banging and banging as it swung round. A strange dream. Not real. Just a dream.

It was a hot summer that year, 1987, and I'd spent the weekends down the end of the back garden sat in a deck chair, my feet in a bowl of water and answering Ian's letters.

I'd go round David's a lot and we would spend afternoons chatting over bottles of wine in his front garden, sat on two dining table chairs with music blaring out of two speakers placed up against his upstairs window. People would walk past and glare at us because of the noise of the music, but we'd be so wrapped up in talking we'd ignore them. I'd usually have Ian's latest letter and we'd talk about it and talk about him and what to write about to him next.

The visiting date was coming up fast and David had just assumed that I wasn't going, so I hadn't mentioned it to him. But I very definitely was going!

I was still writing weekly to Ian and I'd be lying up in bed sometimes till 3 or 4 o'clock in the morning composing letters, long, long letters, sometimes twenty or thirty pages in length. I seemed lately to have some sort of desire aroused in me to understand the nature of things, the soul, and what its journey was, good and evil and whether it really existed.

One night when I didn't have work the following day, I sat up in bed writing till about four o'clock in the morning then drew back the curtains and saw the dark outside getting muzzier and the daylight just beginning to break through, I was sitting there in my room when something strange happened.

I was looking around at my things, eyes falling lightly on the photo of Ian I had next to my bed, the books on my shelf, occultism and the Nazi books that made a sinister match alongside the other books on crime and murder, the gold crucifix I still kept hanging over the dressing table mirror. Then as I kept looking the room faded out, as if it sort of went, and there was just nothing, just a sort of a haze, and I felt kind of dizzy and I leaned my head back on the headboard of the bed. As I straightened my head up I saw something in front of me, like a sort of shimmering in the air. And I felt as if, well as if someone was there, but I couldn't see anyone. There was a slight shimmering in the air and the green mist seemed to disappear and then white out.

I lay there rigid with fear, eyes blinking wide open. There was something there. I tore the sheets back and dived out of bed and grabbed a jumper. I pulled on the jumper, jeans and some old trainers and ran down the stairs and out of the house.

There was something in my room, I knew there was. It terrified me! Was it with me? Was it somehow attached to me?

I made my way down the deserted street. The street lights throwing out an orange glow into the half light. And I ran.
I could hear my own heartbeat pounding in my ears and I turned to see if whatever it was had followed me. I nearly fell as I turned round, then turned back, and carried on running until I reached David's house.

It was nearly five o'clock by then and I rapped hard on David's knocker. It was fully five minutes before the upstairs window opened and he poked his face out.

He saw me and disappeared.

A few minutes later I could see his great bulky body lumbering down the stairs through the glass panel in the door. And he ushered me upstairs without a word then climbed quickly back into bed and covered himself with the duvet, and continued sleeping.

I climbed on the bed and shook him. "Wake up, listen, you'll never guess what happened. I think I've conjured up some spirits." I kept shaking him and eventually he poked his head up from under the covers.

"Don't be stupid, how can you conjure up spirits? It's all those weird books you're reading. I can see I'm not going to get any sleep." He rolled over in bed and winced when he saw the time. "Why do you always have to make your social calls at strange hours of the morning."

He rolled out of bed and padded downstairs and we sat in his rarely visited kitchen as he salvaged some plates from the pile in the sink, ran them under the tap and boiled some eggs in a saucepan that hadn't been washed up yet.

After we'd eaten, we decided to go and take a look at my room again to see if David could see anything.
We drove round there in his beaten up old pick up truck and I made him go upstairs first while I cowered behind him.

The room seemed different to how I'd left it, and the morning sun shining into it seemed to mock the previous fears I'd had about a presence there or anything strange happening.

I sat down on the bed, and thought I must have been dreaming or imagining things, or maybe it was the tiredness of staying up all night. David sat across the room from me, face creased in thought and flicking through the books that were laying open next to my bed. He looked at the covers in surprise. "The occult, since when have you been interested in that?."

"I dunno", I answered, "I think it was after I went to that psychic, and it came true about Ian and then I sort of seemed to be surrounded by people interested in spiritualism, even Maya; and I never knew she was. She said she had often tried to broach the subject with me, but I ignored her."

"It's Brady isn't it?", he demanded.

"What?"
"It's Brady", he started to raise his voice to a shout.

"I told you it's nothing to do with him and shush, my parents are asleep in there", I pointed to the next room. "Look I've never mentioned that sort of thing to him, I don't think he's even interested in it. The Nazi books are the ones I read for him."

"Oh", he said sarcastically, "The Nazi books, oh good that's okay then."
He picked up an L.P. I'd just bought, The Rolling Stones. I put it on the turntable.

"It's Ian's favourite, listen to this track." 'Sympathy for the Devil' blared out, and he stared at me in horror, and I started to laugh. "It's okay, I'm only joking."

"You may be joking but you're asking for trouble, you've got all the props, you have even got letters from Brady - what more could you ask for? All you need now is a ouija board."
He stood up "I'm going, you'd better get some sleep."

I sat on the bed thinking after he'd gone, obviously my imagination had run away with me, but it was probably because of the books I was reading. I didn't finally go to sleep until I put the books Maya lent me outside in the garden shed. I didn't believe what David had said; it was rubbish, but I felt better with it all gone.
The week flew by, and soon it was only five days until the visit, Friday, the weekend, Monday and then Tuesday, the day. I had the weekend lined up to spend with David as usual, and I still hadn't told him about the fact that I was going.

I took my overnight bag round to his house as usual. Then when we'd gone out shopping on the Saturday I'd bought loads and loads of chocolate bars and boxes of chocolate and put them in David's fridge, then bit his head off when he went to eat one.

"They're for the visit" I snapped.

"You're still going?" he asked sadly.

"Yes I am, and I'm going to get a box of sweets a day so I have a load of stuff to take when I go up there."
He didn't mention it any further until the Saturday evening when we were laying in bed watching videos, and he snapped.
Now David had a very bad temper, but it wasn't often that anyone saw it, but when you did you would run for cover.

And that Saturday night he blew.

He shoved me out of bed, then pinned me up against the wall, hand gripped around my neck. My stomach began to purge itself in fear.

"All fucking night long you've been in cloud cuckoo land and I know it's because of that cunt. You can't think of anything but that visit, and you're with me, you should be thinking about me. A girlfriend of mine going up to visit a mass murderer in prison. It's sick, you're sick, this is what he did to kids, this, this and like this!"

He began to beat me again and again around the face until blood came from my nose and began to pump down over my lips.

I started sobbing and gagging, he was nearly strangling me and I was begging him, pleading with him to stop.

"That's it" he sneered cruelly, his face pressed up close to mine.
"This is how his victims begged, this is what he did to others. Now beg, beg me to; . . . . see how they felt."

I knelt down in front of him and begged him to let me go.

He hit me again. "That child killer, that scum is evil. Evil! He's the lowest of the low."
He let me drop and I lay crumpled on the floor sobbing. He turned away to light a cigarette and I bolted.

I ran down the street, then realised I'd left all my stuff there.

I went back and stood in the street, he wouldn't hit me there, and shouted up to the window.

He heard my shouts and the chocolates I'd bought and stored in the fridge came raining down on my head.

It had started to rain by now, starting off light, then getting heavier and heavier, so that great pelts were soaking me, causing blood and make up to run together down my face. I grovelled in the wet and puddles for the chocolates and sweets. Most of the tubes and boxes David had smashed in his hands, but I gathered them up in my arms, picked up my overnight bag he'd thrown out the window and stormed off.

I bent my head against the wind and rain and stumbled down the street towards my house. I could hear David's pick-up being revved up, then the engine as he roared up behind me and drove alongside me, then leant out of the window shouting abuse.

"No-one's going to want to know you."

I ignored him, and bent my head down away from the rain and tried to walk against it quicker.

"I said no-one's going to want to know you", he shouted over to me. "You're standing outside society, if you stand with him, you're on your own."
I turned and screamed at him, "I'm not alone, I'm not alone, I've got <u>him</u>. I stand with him and he's not evil."

I marched on and the rain became thunder and lightning as David stopped his truck and just watched me as I ran along the road dodging the deeper puddles and cowering from the lightning until the rain covered up his windscreen and he could see me no longer.

The train ride up there to Liverpool's Piccadilly was pleasant. I'd treated myself to a first class ticket and most of the long first class coach was empty apart from the odd businessman, head buried in The Times or engrossed in paperwork they'd taken with them in their briefcases.

I was still undecided about what to wear, but in the end settled for the suit I used to go for job interviews in. A black business suit with a white blouse underneath.

I'd taken Monday and Tuesday off work and I decided to book into a hotel and stay in Liverpool on Monday night, then go off to Park Lane for the two o'clock appointment.
The scenery out the window of the train started to tire my eyes in an effort to look at it and made me feel sleepy so I pulled out the book I'd bought at Paddington. It was a new book out by Fred Harrison, a journalist from The Sunday People. 'Brady and Hindley' it was called. And I read with interest the journalist's account of when he had visited Ian Brady.

Ian had told him of a 'Face of Death' a spirit that he had conversed with since he was fifteen and outside a newsagents he said the face appeared to him as a half formed vision in a kind of green mist. The face of death was the spirit Ian had killed for, as sacrifices he had said.

I had read somewhere that Ian had called himself and Myra 'Demonfolk', and I leant my head back against the seat in the train and stared out the window at the landscapes flashing past me; I concluded that the journalist must have been lying. Ian Brady had ignored all the stuff I'd been saying to him about the occult. He just wasn't interested.

The journalist must have made it up. It was ridiculous. 'Face of Death.'

Fred Harrison was the first writer to ever meet Ian. No-one else ever had; not the writer of Beyond Belief or any of the others, all their works were based on hearsay. But Fred Harrison's version of him as gentle and vulnerable and talking about spirits contrasted greatly with the other documented versions of a domineering sadist.

I closed the book. Maybe he'd never even met him; maybe he'd just wanted to be different from the rest. I looked at my watch, it was two o'clock, this time tomorrow I'd be with him myself. And within an hour after that, I'd know everything. I mean you can feel things in people can't you.? I felt sure I'd be able to tell almost everything about him; all in my one hour visit.

The train arrived at Liverpool's Piccadilly soon enough and I took a taxi from the station to a nearby hotel. I went straight up to my room after booking in and decided to stay up there, to get a good night's sleep.

With nothing much else to do I turned the television on, and turned it up when I saw that it was the start of the six o'clock news.

As soon as the picture on the screen flickered into focus, I'd wished I hadn't turned it on. It was the funeral of Pauline Reade. One of Ian Brady's victims they'd found buried on the Yorkshire Moors over twenty five years ago. Fred Harrison had been the one who had kept on at Myra Hindley until she told of the other previously unheard of murders and they'd started searching on the moorland for further bodies. The girl, they had just found. Now, all that was left was a ten year old little boy Keith Bennett, the last victim, still not found.

The face of Lesley Anne Downey's mother flashed up on the screen in front of me. Another mother of one of his victims, a ten year old little girl found buried, over twenty five years ago after going missing for more than two years. What the hell was I doing?!!

I was burning through with guilt, I felt as if I had killed them myself. What was I doing?

Why didn't I just stop myself, it wasn't too late? Why didn't I just go home and put all thoughts of Ian Brady out of my mind. I fell asleep with that thought. And was haunted by dreams of lonely moorlands, mutilated bodies and an axe beating down on my head, again and again, till blood ran down my face in torrents and I fell forward. Then another scene; a small child, screaming in horror, help me, save me, and I reached towards it's outstretched hand and pulled the child towards me. The child's face wet with tears and eyes full of fear and I pulled him close to me, and whispered words of comfort. You're safe my darling now, I won't let anyone hurt you, you're not alone, I'm here, I'm here now. And I woke with a start and remembered the child and felt filled with horror. It was still dark and I switched on the lamp on the bedside table and looked at the clock. Four o'clock in the morning. I left the light on, and made myself a cup of tea from the kettle and tea stuff they had left in the room.

I got back into bed with the tea and picked up the Fred Harrison book I had next to me and started to read through it again, but this time the account of the murders.

93

The stuff was horrific: Children murdered by slitting their necks, an axe, bodies buried face down, in a semi circle way way up on lonely moorlands. Five victims and now two more, one as yet unfound.

I don't think I'd thought of the murders before, I didn't have to, he wasn't real to me, he wasn't Ian Brady, he was the man in the picture so long ago. Was I getting reality confused with fantasy? This was real. The murders were real. The evil was real - and I was part of it.

I shut my eyes and leant back against the bed. I was tired, but the thought of going back to sleep and returning to the nightmares stopped me from turning the light off and trying to get some more sleep.

I flicked through the book in front of me. There were five or six pages of glossy photographs. Ian, one of Myra Hindley, photos of their victims. I turned the page - another little boy, one that I half recognised, and I peered at it harder, till it clicked; the boy in the dream, the one that I went to! I lay staring at it for ages. Surely I must have glanced at it before, and then subconsciously remembered. I looked down at the name beneath the picture. Ian Brady aged seven ...
My mind was playing tricks on me yet again, and I slept fitfully, the bedside light still on, till it got light enough outside and I leant over and switched it off.

The next morning, I woke around six o'clock and threw up straight away. I'd had a nervous stomach since I'd been a kid and I felt tense and wound up. I couldn't get the thought out of my mind, that today I'd be meeting him ...

At two o'clock today I'd be there for a whole hour. All that time. Time spent with a stranger who wasn't a stranger. A man I felt I owed something to for being there, when no-one else was. A man whose blood could be mine - whose loneliness I shared ... A man who I understood, yet, was a stranger. The thought echoed around my head. He was a stranger and I was crazy!

I phoned Alan, "I don't know what to buy him" I started, "I thought I'd have to take something. Can you think of anything, socks or slippers maybe" I started to laugh.

"Look Chris, you're up in Liverpool deciding what present to buy him and others are attending the funeral of one of his victims", he said angrily.

"Look don't phone me again", he went on in his measured Scot's accent, he paused and there was silence at both ends.

"I don't like what you're doing", he said after a while. "If you're going to start making friends with him, then I don't want to know you."

I started crying, I was in the hallway of the hotel and three burly lorry drivers walked past and I turned my face.

"You're all I've got left, I have to phone you", I started urgently - the phone went dead and I held on to it listening to the soft burr till I replaced the receiver.
I looked at my face in the glass above the phone; I looked awful, the make up was mixed in smears down my face and there were dark circles under my eyes where I'd hardly slept.

Alan was the last friend I had, now he'd gone ...

I re-did my make up and made my way into Liverpool Central. It was about ten o'clock in the morning and I had four hours to kill before the visiting time at 2 o'clock. I looked around for something to take him, and couldn't think of anything. Then browsing through the shops it came to me. Of course! Something he'd need; a dressing gown.

I looked around the City shops for ages until I could find one. Then found one I liked in a small retailers but the only size they had was small.

"There's the exclusive men's shop in the centre" the salesman informed me. "You'll definitely get one there, but you'll pay the earth for it."

The shop, when I found it was one of those old fashioned men's type tailors where you could pick the material you wanted and have suits made up for you.

The place smelt of cloth and expensive men's aftershave, and I stood there admiring everything when a tall grey haired gentleman asked if he could help me.

"Yes, I want a dressing gown" I told him. He escorted me over to the far side of the shop and waved to a rack full of a huge selection of men's dressing gowns.

"I'll leave you", he said "To make your choice."

He left me and I tried the various dressing gowns on myself to note the hang of them and see how they looked. There was a full length mirror in front of me and I turned and studied myself from every angle and almost forgot myself as I tried on nearly every one on the rail.

With the brown cotton dressing gown I'd picked wrapped up in a box and tied with string I made my way to the nearest coffee bar and sat flicking through Fred Harrison's book again and waiting for the time to pass. I looked at my watch. It was twelve o'clock, in two hours I would be with him, he was all over the newspapers that day and it added to the unreality of the situation. I drank the coffee and it tasted poisonous in my system as I watched the shoppers, mainly housewives, go about their normal Tuesday afternoon activities.

I could hear the ticking of the huge clock on the wall inside the coffee shop and I wondered whether it was too late to change my mind.

I sat there for what seemed like an age, and the clock hands moved round and I still sat there, and I thought and I thought of what all the others had said. David, Alan, all their shouts of what wrong I was doing. And then I thought back to the dream I'd had, as it flashed into my mind. "I'm here now, I'm here." And I looked up at the clock. It was quarter to two . . .

And I jumped up and I ran.

It was five to two by the time I got to the bus station and asked which bus it was that went to Park Lane. The bus driver told me it would take nearly an hour to get there, and I started to panic, then I turned and saw black cabs.

The black cab driver told me it would take us twenty minutes to get there and I relaxed back in the cab. At least I'd only be fifteen minutes late.

The journey took less than the driver estimated and it was just gone ten past two when he slowed down to go through the huge metal gates of Park Lane.

Park Lane Hospital for The Criminally Insane, the only one in England like it apart from Broadmoor, but where Broadmoor was old and Victorian, this place was new and recently built.

I walked up to the entrance, a large reception area, and I signed a visitors book then; sat down to wait my turn in a separate secured room with a settee, cushioned chairs and huge notice boards warning of prosecution if anything was smuggled into the prisoners inside.

Christine Hart to see 490, Ian Brady, said a deep scouse accent and I got up quickly and moved towards a door that slid upwards then moved into a security cubicle, where I passed over the things I'd bought, and was searched thoroughly by a guard. Then, eventually moved towards an outer door leading into the hospital itself.

A buzzer sounded and the door raised open and it was like finding myself in a different world.

A male nurse stood there to greet me and looked at me stony faced. "This way", he said abruptly, and I followed him as he walked quickly through the hospital. The solid tall grey walls looked menacing and cold, and solitary figures sat about on benches. Around the garden old men with backs bent over and hair that stuck upwards as they muttered to themselves and swayed slowly backwards and forwards.

We walked past various small buildings and a man's screams echoed out the window of one of the buildings as we passed. The nurse glanced back at me and told me to hurry along.

Newman Ward was where Ian was: I'd read he was kept there for his own protection.

He'd been beaten up many times since he'd been there, due to the fact everybody knew of him. So in the end they moved him to the old mens' ward, where he still is. I'd been told he remained in his room for fear of reprisals. I walked through the swing doors that remained unlocked to the ward and then stood in the offices at the end of the corridor.

A short grey haired middle aged man came out and ushered me into his office. "So you want to meet Ian Brady?", he said to me; again the Liverpudlian accent.

He said his name so carefully as if trying to be casual about him yet aware of him. Or maybe it was my imagination. I stared back at him. Then laughed. Nerves. Then stopped. He was staring at me with a look of hatred. I had never experienced before - a stranger and yet he hated me, with a personal deep distaste. I held his gaze, then looked and turned away - so they hated him in here too. I felt sick. These men were strong, and this was their world. I was no match against them - I was on the losing side and I was unsure of whether it was right.

I stood there in his gaze for what seemed like an age, my legs shaking and beads of sweat forming on my upper lip, when he called another nurse. "Call Brady."
I was ushered into a separate room that reminded me of the 'quiet room' at my children's home.

A day room type place with four or five worn armchairs and dull grey painted walls. A lone table with some medical magazines ...

A guard sat across the room from me. I sat down in one of the armchairs wondering where he would sit when he came in.

It seemed like I'd been sitting there for an age, when I turned to look at the guard and he was staring at me, a long penetrating stare of contempt. I shifted around in my seat and my hands stuck to the seat of the chair with sweat. I glanced nervously at him again. He was still staring. I couldn't take this, my stomach started churning, the way it always did when I was nervous or felt fear.

"Does Ian see a lot of people?", I asked him. My voice came out reedy and thin, and I wondered if he had heard me, as he didn't answer straight away - then - "Just his mother . . . and Lord Longford", he said sternly. I twisted around in my seat so I couldn't see him properly then started to look round the room I was in. The door was behind me and I kept turning round to it. Any minute now he'd come through it and I would see him. Things were going round my head of what to talk to him about. And my mouth was becoming dry, then wet, and I swallowed continuously. Then I turned again and the handle turned and I nearly jumped three feet in the air, it was the grey haired man who seemed to be in charge.

"Okay, you can go now, he's in his room, the room at the end of the corridor on the right."

I thought he meant me to go alone, but I looked round and the guard from the room was right behind me as I walked towards <u>his</u> room. The smell in there was the odious sanitary smell of a hospital, tainted with a faint smell of canteen and school dinners, their meals I suppose.

The ceilings were very low, and everything was painted a dull orange. The floor was covered with green carpets, and it all looked new, and sort of bright, yet not welcoming. It all looked like a carpet shop or a D.I.Y centre. All bright and glaring and suffocating.

So this was his reality. This was where he lived, a continuous monotony of orange walls and low, suffocating ceilings, and the smell of school dinners. I walked down the corridor to his room and my legs felt funny, all numb, and I was shaking like a leaf.
I'd read reports and stories in books that he was terrifying and had an evil presence and terrifying eyes.

The short corridor seemed to stretch indeterminably in front of me and it seemed to take years to reach his room at the end, as my imagination ran a picture show of dead children, graves on wasteland, a half human half monster type man with a goat's head, a man's body, and a long, lashing, black, forked tail.

I started sweating and feeling nauseous. I came to his door. It was closed. They'd said that was usual, as he barely came out of his room. The guards took turns to take him his food. Like a monster that no-one ever saw. I turned the handle and went in. He was sitting in a chair facing the window, the sun was beaming in the window shining down on his hair and lighting up the grey in the black.

100

He was big, big shouldered, not like his photos. His hair was curly at the back, slicked back with oil or something. He was dressed in a jacket, cheap navy jacket over a black polo neck sweater and blue jeans, that had holes and patches in them.

He turned, dark glasses covered his eyes, one lens pale, the other dark. You couldn't help but stare at him. I must have stood there for a few minutes just looking, and him looking at me . . . Till I came to. Neither of us spoke. Just stood staring. Both sets of eyes were questioning. And then fascinated.

The guard from the quiet room pushed his head round the door.

"Doctor Strickland's doing his rounds, you'll have to go back to the visitors room."

I stood back and watched as Ian stood up. His height struck me straight away. He was so tall, at least six foot. Funny, everybody had said he was supposed to have been small. And his hair it was like really dark, almost black and swept back, and I think he looked more like he did in that picture I had of him as a kid than the recent ones they had printed in the papers.

I felt sick inside, like my stomach was full of butterflies. I'd expected him to be ill or weak or frail, so I would have felt more at ease, but he was huge, a fully grown man, and I felt stupid, sort of out of my depth.
As he walked down the corridor in front of me towards the visitors' room I'd just come from I stared at his back view and tried to take it all in. I noticed his trousers were way too short and his jacket miles too tight so his arms and legs both poked out too far.

He was walking very slowly and deliberately but with sort of a stoop, and then his stride faltered, and he swayed slightly into the wall. He looked so big, such a giant in that small place with the low ceilings that he looked like a man forced to live in a matchbox. He looked stupid really in there.

In that world full of nearly dead, old men who never spoke. Living in a box, and he was pumped full of drugs to lesson his awareness of his situation, in the way that they drug an animal to get it to go into a box to move it somewhere, but at least that is only temporary.

I watched him walk into the visitors' room at the other end of the corridor, and he fell up against the wall.

And I felt sick.

A man's dignity, totally taken.

At the mercy of strangers who all hated his guts.

I followed him into the visitors' room and sat where I'd sat before.
He sat opposite me, and in front of the guard, so I could still see the guard's contemptuous stare burning through me the whole time I was in there.

We'd been sitting there for about four or five minutes, and still no-one had spoken.

I didn't know what to say, and it felt horrible. I mean, what do you say to a stranger? What do you say to this man; a stranger that seemed so linked to me, and yet I did not know him.

And yet in my letters I'd talked to him about practically everything; talked to him as if I knew him. And I thought about that and I blushed. I wondered what he thought of me. Me and my gushing letters, and now me sitting here with nothing to say. And looking at him like everybody else did, a mixture of horror and distaste. But you couldn't help but stare, and I started to gawp in the rude open way of visitors to Madame Tussauds; gawp openly at the wax figures.

He had his head down and eyes averted and he was looking at his hands that lay crossed on his knees, huge pale bony fingers intertwined with each other. I looked at his face, pale, so pale, almost white like parchment, a roman nose, and a downturned mouth with a jutting out lower lip. He'd removed the dark glasses, and his eyes were strikingly pale. Pale grey, and kind of intense and watchful, but he kept them down all the time and only looked at me quickly when I turned away. And he seemed as if he wanted to make a lot out of the look, as if he wanted to take everything in at a glance.

I looked down and started fidgeting with the hem of my skirt. I didn't know what to say. The minutes kept ticking by and I could see the clock on the wall, and he still hadn't spoken and nor had I.

And the minutes went by until it was nearly twenty minutes gone into the hour of the visiting time.
And then he spoke, and it was like a voice that had somehow lost itself, like he wasn't used to talking, just mouthing the words with his lips. "Did you get here alright?", and he looked at me impassively, then frowned as if he realised what he had said, and looked away again.
I blushed and I could feel my face burning hot.

"The traffic was bad" I said weakly.

The guard behind snorted softly in derision. And I hated him.

I felt stupid. Stupid for being there. Stupid for writing those letters. It was all crazy. I didn't know him. This wasn't the person in my head. This was Ian Brady. And that was real. What was I doing here visiting Ian Brady? It was mad. I had to be mad. Dreams I'd had. And the picture I'd kept for so long. Not him. Not this man in front of me.

The other was in my head. Not real.

This was different.

The dreams were some sort of sleep world where everything is different. A dark fantasy world where you travel to in your sleep. Dreams aren't real. This was real and this was life. And this was Ian Brady ....

And I was mad.

I wanted to go. I had to go.

I looked up and realised that he was speaking.

"They want me to go back on the Moors to search for the other body. I've told the police I can help them find it."
The body . . . the body, the dead body that he squeezed the life out of with those hands. I didn't want him to talk about this; murder wasn't real, it didn't really happen. The room swam in front of me and kept getting fainter until I thought I was going to pass out. And still he was talking, it was a slow soft drawl, almost a whisper, and he seemed to have difficulty in pronouncing the words, the drugs I suppose. "They're digging in the wrong place, they need to saturate the slope with shovels and they'll find him there."

He had said him, him, not it, and I leaned forward and dry retched.

He stopped talking and looked at me.

I kept my face bent down. I had to go. I stood up and looked at the face of the guard.

Can I go?

I didn't look at him, I could feel him sitting there, but I didn't want to look at him or remember him. I'd just go out of there, and forget all of this ever happened. I'd just be me and I'd carry on my life and none of this would matter any more. Then I stood to go out the door. . . . I felt wrong for being there. I just wanted to run out the door.

They needed a guard to escort me out to the gate, so I waited in the corridor.

They left me alone. And there was just him and me, as I waited in the corridor. He came over to me and stood near the door, "Thank you for coming."

I looked away, and he stood there, and I turned completely round so I was turned away from him.

I could feel him. Standing there. And I waited, back towards him, till I heard him walk away back down the short corridor and into his room.
Then I turned.

The relief I had when I walked out of there was indescribable. The effect was almost like crying. It was as if I suddenly exhaled after holding my breath for a long time.

I looked back, as I walked out down the path towards the gate. He'd never do this, he'd never feel that relief, he'd be in there forever now. That place with its smells and the guards with their eyes full of contempt.

I tried to put him out of my mind. So what, what about what he did. He was guilty that's why he was there. There in his box room, with its single bed and hospital blankets and his hospital hand out clothes and his old battered record player.

He'd made all that for himself though; he didn't have to kill people, he could have just behaved like everyone else. No-one made him do it. I walked quickly

105

towards the gate and I noticed the guard that escorted me was one I hadn't seen before, he was short and had a worried look about him. "You can't help but feel horrified by what he did", he started, "They ignore him mostly, it's not their fault, its because of what he did."

I ignored him and carried on walking.

"He was beaten up the other day, on his way to the shop we have here."

I pictured the man I had just seen being hit by others. He was lying on the ground and they were kicking him, and I pushed the picture out of my mind.

"He cries a lot as well", he went on, and again the face of him flashed into my mind; alone, alone in that room, head down, letting tears run down his face.
I thought I was going to retch again. I turned to him and stopped walking, "I'm not interested, I don't know why you're telling me this."

"I censored some of the letters that you sent him, all about good and evil and the soul."

"That was in letters", I interrupted sharply, "It's real though isn't it, the murders, and it was evil. I was wrong. There's no excuse for what he did. He's no different to you or me, and we don't kill anyone, nor does anyone else."

We'd reached the gate and we both stopped and I turned to face him. He looked at me curiously, "Your letters though, it's why he agreed to see you, everybody looks at him in the same way, but you saw him differently - why?"

I had felt that I had to understand him because I owed him something, but I didn't know why . . . I said nothing.

The security door gave out a long buzz and opened automatically, I looked at him and turned away then thought again and turned back and thrust out my hand. He reached out and we shook hands, and he was looking at me intensely.

"Look", I explained, "I'm no different to anyone else, I'm the same as them."

He looked at me, and I thought I saw some sort of sadness in his eyes, and I turned and walked out of there.

I breathed in the air of normality outside the enclosed space of the hospital and I sat outside on the bench near to where the Park Lane bus stopped.

I'd been sitting there for half an hour when the bus came and I got on, glad to be back to normality and sat upstairs in the bus in the front seats and kept the window open. I kept looking out the window and something inside me kept saying, 'He'll never do this, he'll never see that', and another side of me, that felt anger with my thoughts and reasoned that he'd done what he'd done because he was evil, and wrong and bad. So he deserved the pain.

The bus driver started up the bus and it pulled off down the long winding drive away from Park Lane Hospital and I didn't look back.

I took the eight o'clock Liverpool Piccadilly to London Kings Cross train and gazed out the window on the long journey home, until eventually it got too dark so I turned and looked at the other passengers on the train, dotted around me in their seats. A young girl sat reading, long dark hair wound into a plait, falling down over her shoulder. A couple half asleep leaning against each other, and a young mother talking baby talk softly to her young child.

I stared at them all in turn for what seemed like an age. There they were, nice people, all leading nice lives, and striving for goals that were pleasant and decent and rewarding.

They were good people and had no knowledge of the bad and the evil and the sadness I'd somehow got myself involved in . . . no knowledge of where I'd been, who I'd been to see . . . who I was!

I turned and stared at my reflection in the darkened window of the train. I wasn't bad looking, quite pretty. I could find a man who would show me love, I could have a beautiful baby like the woman next to me. But not if I carried on, not if I carried on down the road I was on at the moment. I didn't want 'him' and his sadness, I wanted to have what they had, the people around me. I pulled out a book and started to read it until I realised that it was "The Astral Body" by A E Powell and I closed it and slid it down the back of the seat next to me. I had no further use for it, no more stupid weird books. No more Ian Brady, I'd just stop writing to him.

I was me, and this was my life and it was all I had. And after the orphanage, after the cold, loneliness of the past, I actually had a chance now to have a decent normal life with a family and a home, like a normal girl, like the girl on the train with her long dark plait and her air of complacency. It felt like I was being given a chance all over again, like when Mr. Hart first took me out of the orphanage. . . . Take it!

Wednesday morning and I was back in work, at my desk, the familiar office routine and I felt happy and relaxed and joined in with all the office gossip and whizzed though my pile of work on my desk with renewed energy.

I stopped off after half past five with the others in The George next door to work. Lucy, a tall blonde who I usually sat next to, called me over and I laughed and chatted to her over halves of lager, then went next door and bought a kebab from the Turkish take-away and went to catch the tube.

As soon as I got in the door I saw it. I'd been dying to get in and I felt tired and woozy from the lager, and I just wanted to get to bed, but it was there.

I didn't think he'd write, not if I didn't write to him. What was this? He couldn't just write to me at will.

'I sit alone in my room, a lot of time, sometimes I can go for weeks and I don't need to speak, I forget how to. I am sorry for your wasted journey. You are very beautiful, I enjoyed your visit very much'.

I threw it away.

The days went by and then the weeks until it was late August 1987. It was still hot and everyone was out and about sporting their deep tans from the good weather that year. I'd had no thought of Ian Brady after the visit and only one other letter had come after that. I'd returned it unopened.

That was it, that part of my life was over. It was crazy but something that I didn't have to think about any more.

Ian Brady had forgotten me and I had forgotten him and it was all over.

It was about three weeks later that I walked into the newsagents one morning and saw his face over all the newspapers that day. I stopped dead when I saw it and felt sort of strange. It was weird to think I'd actually met him and he was real to me and here he was plastered over all the daily newspapers. I bought a copy of my usual paper and leant up against the wall of the newsagents and read the story.

He'd confessed in a letter to the BBC that as well as the five children he'd murdered he had also killed five more people, adults this time. Two women, pushed into canals, bludgeoned to death, and two men, one shot in the head and the other hit with a brick again and again on the back of the head. The headline ran across the front of the page and read "I killed five more." Then there were the pictures, one of him, then one of two women whose bodies had been found around that time when he'd said he had murdered them.

I studied the faces of the two women both fairly young and pretty, and I felt an incredible guilt:

Ever since I'd stopped writing to him I'd felt as if I was denying something within myself as if denying the very purpose I'd been born for.

And yet, here was more murders, more evil. I felt torn inside between the feeling I was doing wrong by not contacting him and the feeling that he was bad and evil and I was glad I was not involved with his world and his destructiveness, happy to have him out of my life, out of my world.

I breathed a sigh of relief that day. I went to work as usual and kept reminding myself that I was an average 23 year old, there was nothing different about me, I was like all the rest; nothing different, not even a strange alliance with a mass murderer locked away in an asylum under maximum security for killing so many, so long ago. And I'd forget I ever wrote to him and ever met him, I'd put it all out of my mind, and not even think of it again. I'd just carry on my life and do things like everyone else did and try to find some sort of happiness.

If you believe in destiny and purpose you will believe that sometimes and in certain cases things happen to push us down a path that we are reluctant to go and yet we are compelled to go. I don't know whether that is what happened way back but all I know is I intended to ignore a deep feeling and near compulsion within me and to have no further contact with Ian Brady.

Until something happened that ensured I would have no choice in the matter ...

It was two o'clock in the afternoon and it was one of those sleepy Sunday afternoons where not even the sound of lawn mowers and ice-cream vans are audible. All was sunny, peaceful and still, and I climbed out of bed and padded downstairs to make myself a cup of tea and see if anyone else was around.

The house was dead except for the grandfather clock ticking away in the front room. I tried the door and it was locked. My parents always locked it when

110

they went out, along with their bedroom door, it made me feel cheap and mean, in a way or somehow like an intruder or a lodger, who wasn't really trusted. I suppose I was really . . . just a lodger.

They'd gone out to church, like they did every Sunday, so I took the opportunity to sit in the kitchen and make myself some tea and cereal and eat it there instead of taking it up to my room like I always did.

I went to turn on the radio but then thought better of it, the peace of the day and in the house was beautiful. I didn't want to spoil it. I'd read the papers instead. The Sunday papers. They always had the Sunday Mirror and the People, and I usually didn't bother reading them, they were always full of the rich and famous and what they'd been up to and it didn't really interest me.

That day though, I started flicking through them, first the glossy magazines that came with them with their photos of glamorous celebrities and showbusiness gossip, and then I thumbed though the newspapers, first The Sunday Mirror, then I picked up The Sunday People.
It's difficult really to described the feelings I felt at that moment....The moment I saw it . . . There in hard print·. . . It was one of those things that you don't even let yourself think about. It seems so outside of the realms of possibility, that I had never even in my wildest dreams considered such a thing.

The headline of a news story at the top of page five in The Sunday People read 'BRADY WOOS GIRL BY POST'- I think my first reaction was 'Oh, he's got a girlfriend, that's strange', read the story with interest. They were describing a girl, in her early twenties, blonde haired, who had been writing to him, then gone up to Liverpool to meet him'. 'Brady is fascinated by her, and she has written extensively to him. No-one can quite believe this friendship is as strong as it is', what the hell is this strong connection between them?.

'She is the first visitor apart from Lord Longford and his mother he has allowed to visit him for nine years'.

And I remember thinking, no that's wrong! That Fred Harrison, the journalist, met him two years ago, and I wouldn't let my mind grasp it.

'She is the first visitor he has allowed to visit him in nine years, early twenties and blonde haired'. I read it and re-read it, and tried to block out the realisation that was coming into my head.

And then I read the last sentence they'd written 'as yet this girl remains unnamed'.

This girl! This girl . . . . was me! It was me! It couldn't be! It just couldn't be! And I read and re-read that story over and over, hoping in some way it would all of a sudden change and I'd realise that I had been imagining what I'd read. But it didn't. It stayed the same . . . it was about him and me and they wanted to know why. Why were we so close?

I think I must have sat there for ages hoping in some way that it would turn out to be a dream.

I remember when I'd first written to him and in one of his early letters he'd written, 'You must think of the consequences of writing to me'.

And I remember I'd thought that he meant with God, and me going against God by writing to him, and I'd visited the church soon after he'd said that.

I never thought, never dreamed of this. The press, I had no knowledge of these people, they lived in a different world. Surely the newspapers only wrote about famous people, not everyday people, like me. The phrase 'as yet unnamed' was the one that hit me hardest. My name! Surely if these people had have found out everything else, wouldn't it be just as easy for them to find out my name?

This story must be to interest people, then tomorrow they would probably name me.

The next day was Monday and I hadn't slept, just sat up in bed thinking and then laid down face in the pillow, sobbing.- It was serious what I'd done, and now I was going to pay the price for it. And I was scared. What if they somehow found out about what is being said about my birth.
The whole nation hated Ian Brady and here was I, my name soon to be in the newspapers for being who I was . . . And who was that?

The friends I'd lost over the last few months would be nothing compared to complete strangers coming up to me in the street; almost certainly to deride me and abuse me . . . where could I hide? . . . what could I do?

My foster parents would be mortified. They were strict Catholics, who attended church regularly and had never done anything wrong in their lives. They had always lived in the same road, a small tight knit community. The shame they'd feel, their daughter, their foster daughter, linked to Ian Brady. And would the papers print the reason? They were old, and my father had a weak heart and they had taken me in and given me a home when I was in the orphanage, then later after the overdose, and this was how I was going to repay them.

The scandal and the shame.

They, like everyone in Britain looked upon Ian Brady as 'the lowest of the low', which is how they usually put it, and to be associated with him would cause them the utmost shame.

Me, well that day, I didn't feel shame, I just felt a deep and utter terror and fear; I wasn't ready to stand apart from society and declare my differences and beliefs and for the good reason that I wasn't sure what my differences and beliefs were. Let alone lean on them to give me comfort and strength . . .

113

I didn't know why I'd first written to him. It seemed it had all been going on with him for so long, I had no real idea of how it all started. Maybe I was mad. I froze in fear at the thought and a picture flashed into my mind. The headline 'Mad Christine', with a photograph of me underneath with dead, drugged eyes, locked away in another institution for my own protection.

I had to speak to someone. I had no idea what to do. I was up that Monday morning by six o'clock and had run round the newsagents to flick though all the tabloid newspapers. I stood in the shop, eyes running over page after page of daily news stories.

There was nothing there.

Then I walked across the road to the public pay phone and phoned Alan, surely he would speak to me now, I was in such trouble.

He gave me nothing but good advice.

"Look, all you have to do is disappear, there probably won't be an article, but in case there is, just don't be around, disappear up to Scotland for a while, go somewhere where they don't get newspapers", he intoned in his measured Scots accent.

I thanked him over and over and hung up. Thank God for Alan.

I opened the door of the phone box and walked slowly back home. It was still early, half past six but barely anybody was up.

The sun was already up though and it shone brightly, the promise of another scorcher of a day, and I relaxed a little and thought warmly of Alan. I remembered how I'd sat next to him at work at the small detective agency in Ealing, before the company expanded and moved offices.

We'd been based in an old Victorian building and there were four of us who did telephone investigations in a small office. Tina, who was in charge of us, Alex, Alan and me.

He was about two years older than me and from the minute he'd started working with us I'd warmed to him. He seemed so wise, so, sort of clever, that when I'd left the agency and moved to another he'd been the one I'd kept in contact with. He'd been the one I'd gone for drinks with, hours spent discussing this and that over endless glasses of beer. He'd been the one I phoned for advice or whenever I was in trouble. He was like a big brother to me, and I'd loved him so much that even when his mother died and his sister phoned him at work, I'd locked myself in the loo away from the others and sobbed for ages at the thought of his suffering.

I reached home, looked around my bedroom and decided he was right, I'd have to go away. I looked around for my building society book, I had eight hundred pounds, my rainy day savings. I slipped it into my handbag and began to pack a suitcase full of clothes and things I'd need.

It was funny really because about a month ago, when I'd still been friends with David I'd said to him "I think that soon I'm going to be leaving my room, I feel it." And it's as if something inside of me is saying to me, not to mind this, as they like my possessions, they don't matter at all, when I think previously they did.

And it was odd! I was leaving just like the premonition told me I was going to do.

It took me about half an hour to pack all my stuff into a suitcase and I left out a nightdress to sleep in that night - today I'd arrange the travel times and tickets and tomorrow I'd just go.

I phoned in work and told then I had personal problems and that I'd be off work for two weeks. Steve, an ex-policeman who ran the detective agency laughed at me down the phone "You're never here anyhow. I'm used to it."

I promised him I'd be back at my desk in a fortnight and producing good work, and he wished me well and hung up. Again I smiled to myself over how lucky I was: A job I enjoyed, which was more than a job, it was a career with interesting possibilities, and a brilliant boss and good people to work with.

I went to the building society that day and drew out three hundred pounds of my savings and found out the times of the coaches to Scotland from Victoria.

The coach left Victoria at 10 o'clock the next morning, and I decided against purchasing a ticket but to get one the following morning. I slept fitfully that night but I still slept, whereas I didn't the previous night.

I tossed and turned a lot in my sleep and remember experiencing a sort of feeling of things touching me all over; just lightly brushing my skin. It was more than a dream. I always dream, but this time it was as if I was fully awake and there were presences all around me as I slept.

Morning soon came and I woke up with a strange surge of apprehension, then told myself I had nothing to worry about. Today, in a few hours, I would be sitting on a coach bound for Scotland and staring out the window and hoping the driver wouldn't go too fast on the motorway.

I went round the newsagents again early that morning to see if there was anything in the newspaper. Nothing! And I relaxed again as I walked back home and started planning in my mind, the best time to leave the house to be at Victoria by ten.

As soon as I reached the house, I heard the phone ringing and I remember thinking that it was funny, the phone ringing so early as it was barely seven o'clock. And then being even more surprised when my mother handed it to me and told me that it was Alan.

I took the phone from her and laughed straight away, "It's okay Alan, I'm going today, I've got my case all packed."

He sounded strange, sort of distant and not his usual self.

"Christine, look, I've had an idea. If you go up to Scotland they might just wait till you come back to do a story. I think the best idea is if you get some advice off someone I know, he used to be a journalist, so he'll know what the best thing is for you to do."

I had always followed Alan's advice and that day was no exception. He told me to meet him at one o'clock for lunch at a pub in Ealing next to the office.

One o'clock and I was there, sharp. I'd bought my suitcase with me and I had it planned in my mind that I'd carry on up to Victoria after I'd had lunch with him. I wanted to see him anyway, I hadn't for a long time and it would be nice to say goodbye.

It was about quarter past one and he suddenly appeared as if from nowhere. Funny really, something seemed sort of wrong and he wouldn't look at me, wouldn't meet my eyes, then when I tried to hug him as I always did he moved away and looked straight past me.

"Chris, I'm sorry I can't make it for lunch, I'm too busy."

I breathed a sigh of relief, so that was what was wrong with him, he felt guilty because he couldn't meet me after all. "That's okay", I smiled at him, "It's nice to see you anyway."

And then he turned and walked towards the offices and I thought "What", he hasn't even said goodbye, what's up? And then he turned and he just stood

117

there looking at me, and I turned, and that's when I saw them.

Two men and one woman, sort of dressed up, they looked really important like some sort of city workers. I peered at them, and as I did, they all immediately stopped talking and turned to look at me, as if the previous talking and the way they had appeared to have been absorbed in conversation was all some sort of charade. And then I looked down and I saw in front of one of them a large camera with loads of flashes and it suddenly dawned on me. I was frozen to the spot, and while my mind told me to run, it was as if my legs wouldn't carry me. I seemed to be running out of time as they got up in unison and moved towards me. Behind them I could see Alan, just standing there watching. And I thought 'No, not Alan, not my friend, not this'. And my first reaction was to cry, and then I sort of shook myself and picked up the case and ran . . . All these years, of trust and affection and thinking that the guy was a friend, a true friend, and now this. He had set me up.

I turned as I reached the main road and one of them was right behind me, tall with gingery hair and a saggy face, about forty five. I turned back and ran across the busy main road dodging the flashing cars, beeping their horns and screeching to a halt in front of me. I could see a bus just pulling away from a stop a few yards up the road and I lugged the suitcase and ran as fast as I could towards it. I managed to throw the suitcase on to it, but grabbed on to the pole with my hands and forgot to jump on, and the bus moved on with my suitcase on it and I stood in the road looking at it. I let out a sob, and watched the bus, then watched it slow down again as the traffic stopped when the lights changed. I ran towards it with all my determination and jumped on just as it jerked into motion and roared off at quite a speed. I breathed hard and looked around. The ginger haired man that had been chasing me, stood in the road and watched the bus.

I put the suitcase in the rack downstairs then climbed up to the top deck of the bus and sat on the back seat. The bus conductor, a tall West Indian, came round and collected the fares and grinned at me good naturedly. "You look as if you just seen a ghost" he laughed. I smiled back at him and settled in my seat. Everything was okay. I didn't have to talk to them if I didn't want to. I'd just go home and go back to work as normal. They couldn't hurt me. I'd lost them and that was that.

The memory of Alan, was a painful one, and I tried to put him out of my mind. My big brother, my best friend. Why? I felt like crying. I wondered whether he felt that we were friends, and, had I been just a nuisance who phoned him for advice all the time. I felt an intense pain at this betrayal. Why? Why? Why had he done what he'd done?

The bus moved along the Uxbridge Road towards Hayes slower than usual, and I leant my lead back on the back of the seat and let my gaze wander out the side window, when a dreadful thought hit me, and I turned quickly and looked out the back window of the bus and down on the traffic below. That's when I saw him, looking straight at me and smiling! The man who'd chased me from the pub.

I turned round in my seat in horror, it was him, him sitting next to the other man he'd been with who was driving a long dark green jaguar. I sat there trembling and started to cry and shake uncontrollably. I was scared out of my wits. Who were these people that seemed so ruthless and so frightening. There was nothing I could do, the only exit on the bus was the back door and they had it covered, what were they going to do to me.

I was sitting there crying and the bus conductor who had previously been so friendly glanced over at me, "Are you all right love?."

I wiped the tears away and looked up at him. I was hysterical! It wouldn't do me any good if I continued to panic. "I'm okay" I whispered back and I straightened myself up and tried to think about what to do. I looked round quickly then turned back. The car had moved even nearer in the traffic and now was directly behind the bus. There was absolutely no way out. The bus seemed to slow down in its journey and take longer than I had ever known it to take. And I feared that one of the people in the green jaguar would jump out and board the bus and get me that way.

Eventually, after what seemed like an age, we drew up to Hayes Roundabout, and I jumped off the bus and grabbing the suitcase, ran as fast as I could.

I dodged in and out of the shoppers along the busy main road and managed to dodge down an alleyway in between the shops.

I crouched there for about an hour at the end of the alleyway, breathing hard, with my heart thumping away in my mouth, till I got up and slowly walked towards the bus stop so that I could catch another bus to get to Hayes Town.

I caught a bus almost straight away and got off at Hayes Station, then made my way towards Bourne Avenue via the back way through the quiet suburban roads to my house.

By the time I'd got to about a mile from my house, I relaxed. It was around three o'clock in the afternoon and very hot and after all the running, my T-shirt clung to me and my face felt burning hot with the sun beating down on it.

The traffic on the roads was still fairly busy as the local office workers out to lunch, slowly made their way back to their offices for the afternoon. I thought of work and how they'd all probably just be on their way back from the pub by now, and leaned my head back and pointed my face at the sun. It was very hot, and the suitcase wasn't helping much. The two miles from Hayes Station to my house seemed like twenty two.

And I breathed a sigh of relief as my road came into sight. Then, I'd just turned the corner into my road when suddenly the thought hit me. If Alan had set me up then he could have just as easily given them my home address.

I was at the top of my road and I began to run. The suitcase banging painfully against my ankle as I dragged it along behind me. The house was quite near the corner of the road and as I ran down the front path and fumbled with the key in the lock, I heard car doors slam and they came running across the road. I just got the door open and managed to close it, as they reached it.

And then I collapsed on the stairs frantically sobbing and exhausted, from the running.

I thought that I had never been so scared in my life, and nothing could ever be as bad as this or could be any worse. Then I heard the woman journalist, as she opened the letter box and shout into it.

"We know, you believe Brady's your father", I sat there numb with fear.

She banged on the door again, then flicked open the letter box and put her mouth to it. She was hard - really hard and she terrified me. The coldness and hardness in her voice filled me with fear. How could I tell this woman anything? I was so terrified of her.

There was shouting again, through the letter box, this time a man's voice. "Look if you don't let us in and tell us the story, you'll have everyone in Fleet Street outside the door. The wolf pack they call them, and that's what they're like. We're your friends, we only want to help you."

I moved from the stairs through to the kitchen and jumped as I saw the one that had chased me standing at the back door and trying the handle to get in.

I put the bolts on the door then walked away backwards never taking my eyes off him, then shut the kitchen door and moved into the back room.

121

I leant up against the wall in the dining room then crouched down on the floor like a cornered animal. They were banging on the front door and on the back door and shouting things all about him being my Father.

I ran into the hallway, grabbed the phone and ran up the stairs with it and phoned Alan's number. He answered and I sobbed down the phone hardly able to speak. "They're saying he's my Father, Alan, They're saying he's my Father." I was dry retching and shouting at him and I heard the phone go dead, and I dialled the number again, then thought again and slammed the phone down.

I sat on the top of the stairs crying and shaking until I noticed something, the banging seemed to have stopped. I got up and the thought of my parents hit me for the first time, they'd be back soon. I couldn't put them through all this. They were so old, and my foster father had a weak heart, he'd die from the shock. He'd die and it'd be all my fault.

I jumped up and went to the front door. There didn't seem to be anyone around.

So they had gone. They'd given up and gone. Thank God.

I turned the lock on the door slowly and pulled it open just a crack to see if their car had gone as well. Then as I did I felt it burst open and I jumped back and as I did so, he appeared, the very first one of them I'd seen.

He stuck his foot in the door and pushed himself in. "Look", he said, "We don't want to hurt you, we're on your side, but if you don't tell us your story, you'll have them all out here."

I started to cry again, tears were running quickly down my face and I made no effort to check them.

122

"Do you want us to take you somewhere? I don't know if anyone else you live with, is in."

"My parents", I said, "And my foster father has got a weak heart, he's already had one heart attack."

"Well then look", he offered, "We'll take you up to our offices, I think that's best, don't you, and then you can tell us this thing about Brady being your father." I gasped at his last sentence, "Who told you that?"

"Alan's already told us, so there's no point in denying it. You've been writing to him, or trying to write to him since you were a little girl so Alan tells us. By the way have you got any proof of this?"

I started to sob again, "Look he's not, Alan's wrong. He's not my Dad. I haven't got a Dad. I grew up in an orphanage."

He cast a glance at the other two journalists. "So you grew up in an orphanage believing he was your Father."

"No, I .... I", and I stopped.

What could I say? Is that what happened? Did I think that? The reason why I'd kept his picture all those years ago. Why? Why? Not even I knew. What had the social worker said? 'A notorious criminal' My mum was so ashamed that she wouldn't even put his name on the certificate.

"They told me my Father was in prison", I offered, "But they didn't say it was Ian."

"You just thought it was" the woman journalist said, "But why? Did you come from the same area?"

I thought back. My mother was born in Hull in Yorkshire where Ian had gone to borstal. I'd found that out later, but I'd never thought anything of that. It was enough for the reporters. They told me to lock up the house and come with them, and the next minute I was sitting in the back of the long green Jaguar that I'd been running from all that day looking out the window and feeling dizzy and sick with fear over the trouble I was in and the events that lay ahead.

The smooth Jaguar weaved expertly through the late afternoon traffic, and I caught the eye of a girl in the car next to ours. I eyed her enviously, she looked happy and carefree, and at this moment, I would have given anything to change places with her.

People moved up and down Kensington High Street in the bright sunlight going about their business, like a normal day. A normal day to them. Yet for me it was as if my whole world had been uprooted; or was about to be.

We got to the Mirror Group building that was in Holborn in the City and I got out of the car in the car park with them. There were three of them there then and I looked at them each in turn: Ted Hynds, the one who had chased me with his ginger hair and public school accent. Phil Hall, with his grey beard and half disguised cockney accent and smooth good looks. And the girl, slim, about thirty and immaculately turned out with dark blonde colouring. They all had an air of sophistication and a kind of hardness about them. They seemed cynical and uncompromising.

I think that's what frightened me most about them.

How could I explain how I'd felt about a fantasy man in a picture? How could I tell them how I'd wondered whether I was good or evil? How could I explain that I felt different to others as if I didn't belong and I'd thought he was the same? A different kind. And how I thought I could help him. How he eased my loneliness all those years in the orphanage and how I wanted to find a way to do something for him in return.

And then later how I'd visited him and wondered what I was doing. Getting caught in a dream, and confusing fantasy with reality. How I'd stopped doing it. And how when I'd stopped doing it, I felt as if I was denying something in myself, as if denying my whole purpose.

And I sat there, that afternoon, in their office with the thick carpet and the air conditioning and the strip lighting surrounded by them and their worldly faces and sophistication and cynicism, and I knew. I knew they'd look at me as if I was crazy. I realised in the end I didn't have to say.

Alan had given them the reason why he thought I was writing to him and they had their story, and it was the story they wanted.

All they wanted off me now, was what it was like growing up and having no-one. And I knew all about that. And I told them. Reliving the pain of the loneliness in all the detail I could remember. And they sat there, with their endless cigarettes and their cold stares and their notepads on their knees and every so often jotted down things that I had said. Until they decided I'd said enough.

The events that followed that afternoon seemed to follow each other in a kind of blurr.

They said that they wanted me to stay with them in a hotel 'to watch me', they said in case anyone else in Fleet Street had found out about me.

Found out about me! I'd wondered what they meant. Surely my life was of no interest to others. Why were they making such a fuss?

They drove me back to my parents' house and told me to pack for a few days.

So I just went to pick up the suitcase with all my stuff in that I'd packed earlier for Scotland. I went back there, and I went in and I said to my parents that I was going away for a while like before, with my work. They said goodbye and I looked at them. They looked so old, and I felt a kind of heartache for them. How easy and beautiful life would have been, if they had been able to have their own children. Instead, they had been landed with me. Me with my craziness and me with my strangeness. I looked at them and said goodbye and blinked back tears as I closed the front door behind me as if it would be the last time that I'd ever see them.

They took me after that to a hotel in Swiss Cottage. I sat alone in the room and looked at the baked potato fish I'd ordered from room service. I couldn't eat it.

The room was quite a nice one, Trusthouse Forte, with pink walls and matching bedspread. I went into the bathroom and looked at myself in the mirror with loathing, and wondered how I'd managed to get myself into such a mess.

I couldn't cry, the amount of tears I'd shed during the day had left me exhausted and sort of numb.

I went back into the room and laid on the bed.

It seemed that I lay there for nearly three hours, just staring at my reflection in the mirror opposite the bed.

I felt totally at the mercy of the three business-like people in the rooms adjacent to mine.

Please don't ruin my life. Please!

I wanted to sleep but every time I lay my head down and drifted into shallow slumber, my body would awaken after a minute with a severe jolt and it made proper sleep impossible, so I gave up and just sat there, thinking.

What would everyone say? How badly would it affect my foster parents? I felt nauseous and headachey from lack of sleep and sat up rigid on the bed until it began to get light outside and the clock showed eight o'clock.

It was about half past eight when I heard a sharp knock on the door. It was the older of the journalists, Ted Hynds.

"Oh good, you're up", he said as I opened the door. "Look, what we want you to do is go up and see Brady. We'll fly you up there and when you get in with him, we want you to hand him your birth certificate and ask him if he is your father"

I started to cry again. My eyes were red raw and puffy and too sore to rub, so I just cleared them by pressing them against the back of my hand. The idea of going up and seeing him again, especially as I hadn't replied to any of his letters was a horrible one.

He saw my reaction and started to get impatient with me. "I'm sorry we have to do this, I know it's hard on you, but this is a good story and we want to know Brady's reaction to the possibility of him having a daughter."

I sat down on the bed and looked up at him, "Please, I've told you, he may not be my father."

He opened his mouth to reply but was interrupted by the other journalist Phil Hall who came in then, and looked at me and smiled. "The photographers here Ted, and he's bought Sue with a couple of dresses. Shall we? . . ."

A tall dark curly headed man came in to the room with an array of expensive looking camera equipment round his neck and carrying a huge silver case, and various tripods, and behind him a short blonde girl with spiky hair bleached to almost platinum blonde.

I was ushered into a chair and the girl started pulling all creams and lotions from a large pink vinyl bag and began to apply cream to my face then tissued it off and applied some toner lotion and then moisturizer. "What look do you want, what's the story?" she shouted over to Ted, who stood over the other side of the room, talking to Phil and the photographer. I blushed immediately and prepared for her reaction when he said it's a story about Ian Brady, when he shouted back "As sexy as possible Sue." And I thought, how odd; that doesn't really go with the story.

The girl worked on my face for about fifteen minutes applying shadows and lipstick from a huge selection of every colour and make she had in a large silver tool box in front of her. Then she pulled out some tongs and plugged them in to heat and she started painting my nails with a deep red nail polish. After she'd tonged my hair into what felt like curls, she held up a dress for me to slip into.

I went into the bathroom and pulled the black and silver dress on and turned to look at myself in the mirror and almost recoiled in horror. I'd never really been conscious of a cleavage before, and I'd certainly never wore a dress that purposely gave me one.

I unlocked the bathroom door and came out slowly, I looked like a prostitute, surely they didn't want me to look like that. I looked at Ted and Phil and noticed Ted wouldn't meet my gaze and looked at the floor "That looks great", he said, and I wondered what was going on.

I felt out of my depth with these people. One minute they behaved as if they were friends, the next minute they behaved coldly, indifferently, uncaring.

"Please", I whispered, "Please don't make me wear it. It looks awful." The

make up girl shot me a glance of sympathy, "Try it back to front." I undone a few of the buttons and twisted it round and looked over at Ted.
"I suppose it's okay, but for god sake smile. It's not the end of the world."

The photographer had assembled most of the equipment and I sat in front of a huge sheet he'd pinned to the wall, and he moved round me and started taking pictures.

He must have taken about twenty or thirty when he put down the camera and looked at me, "You look like you're going to cry; it's no good. I can't get a good picture with you so unrelaxed."

Ted moved over to the phone and dialled for the room service. Five minutes later a porter arrived at the door carrying a tray with a half bottle of vodka on it and a jug of fresh orange juice.

I was told I wouldn't taste the vodka, as it would make me more relaxed so I could be photographed.

With the fact that I hadn't slept at all and I hadn't had any breakfast, two glassfuls made up by Ted began to make me feel really woozy . . . It wasn't long before I became quite relaxed and co-operative. I posed as requested and eventually he managed to take some pictures he was satisfied with. The next arrangement was a taxi to Heathrow so I could be on the one o'clock flight to Liverpool.

I changed from the dress into jeans and a T-shirt but didn't have time to comb my hair straight, or wipe off the deep flashy make up.

We got straight into a black taxi in front of the hotel, and the driver was given orders to drive as fast as possible.

Phil Hall was the one who was going with me up to Liverpool and he sat

129

silently in the seat beside me in the taxi.

I had my birth certificate with me in my handbag and I thought of the orders, I had to show it to Ian. I didn't want to, it'd be stupid. I wasn't sure whether Ian was my Father, but they weren't prepared to believe me.

I thought of how I'd ignored his letters. I didn't want to see him.

"Phil, look this is stupid", I started, "I don't want to go, I really don't."

"I wouldn't put you through this, but you know what Ted's like, and if you don't do this, he'll go head and print that you undoubtedly are his daughter."

"He can't do that", I protested.

"He can and he will, so that's why it's best to find out from Ian, one way or the other."

I sat back in my seat. Ian Brady was the most hated man in Britain, and if they were going to say I was his daughter they would hate me too. I'd be part of him and they'd want to kill me as he killed others. To get back at him through me.

My stomach surged with fear. Whatever happened I'd have to get Ian to say he'd never had a girlfriend called Mary and he'd never been near Hull after his borstal release. Then I'd tell them what he said and they'd have no story. They wouldn't print anything. They didn't believe me, but they'd believe him.

The journey up there was horrible, the taxi was late getting there and we missed the one to Liverpool so we had to fly to Manchester and then have another journalist from the Sunday People office in Manchester who knew the way to Park Lane, to drive us there to save time.

The journalist who greeted us as we came through into arrivals at Manchester airport was in his late forties, overweight with short dark thinning hair. He led

us to the car park and a white cavalier. Phil sat in the front and I was relegated
to the back seat, when my glance fell to the clock on the dashboard, it was two
thirty and visiting hours ended at four o'clock.

The fat journalist had absolutely no idea of the way from Manchester to
Liverpool, so we sat there for a good five minutes trying to work out the best
route to take while pouring over an A to Z.

Phil was like a cat on hot bricks as he sat in the front seat, nervous in case he
didn't manage to get me there on time. I sat in the back, with my gaze fixed on
the clock on the dashboard, the tension in the air became more and more
intense.

I glanced again at the clock. It was quarter to three and we weren't even half
way there; there was no way we'd get to Liverpool by four o'clock.

I leant my head forward in between the two front seats, "Doesn't anyone care
we'll be late."

"It doesn't really matter", Phil announced smugly, "In fact it'll be better, he'll
think you're not coming, be upset, then surprised and pleased when you're late."

I glared at the back of his head. Then turned and stared out the window.
The lack of sleep and the two vodkas I drunk were making me feel sick and
dizzy with tiredness, and the daylight seemed brighter and I felt sort of dirty
and grotty in the way you do if you miss a night's sleep.

We eventually reached Liverpool. Then we had to stop and ask passers by the
way to Park Lane.

They dropped me at the end of the drive leading up to the hospital, and drove
the car off up the road, where they said they'd be waiting for me when I came

out.

For the first time since I'd met them, I'd been let out of their sight and I felt a surge of desire to run, but then I thought, no, stupid, they've already got your photograph and most of a story, they'd print it anyway. At least doing this I had a chance to stop them.

My boots crunched into the gravel as I walked up the long drive to the huge reception area of Park Lane and I walked up to the guard behind the desk, gave my name and told them I was a visitor for 490, Ian Brady.

He looked at me in the usual way the guards there did when I told them who it was I was visiting, but this time he was in the right. It was five minutes to four and visiting hours ended at four.

"You're too late" he snapped abruptly in a thick scouse accent, "Visiting hours end at four."

"Yes but I've still got five minutes, look", I pointed up to the large clock behind his head.

He glared at me angrily, then picked up a grey coloured phone in front of him, said something down it and then slammed it back down again. "Okay, you've got five minutes." A buzzer sounded in front of me and a young guard stepped forward to escort me to the security section.

"Have you got anything on you", he said as he ran his hands over my white T-shirt and jeans. "Take off the boots." I took off the white cowboy boots I had on and shook them out.

He stepped back satisfied, "Okay, and you've been here before so you know that's not allowed", he pointed to the lemonade bottle, and I handed it over obediently.

The glass hatch rose up before me and I stepped inside the hospital grounds; the fresh air hit me, and I looked around hopefully for my friend again, the nurse who had escorted me before, but instead, a red haired young man dressed in a short white tunic and black trousers came towards me.

He escorted me through the hospital to Newman Ward, which is at the back of the hospital, and we said nothing on the long walk over there.

As soon as I walked in the ward I caught sight of Ian, going to get his dinner. He looked very vulnerable the way he stood there not really fitting in with his surroundings and I remembered the way I'd ignored his letters and felt a sense of guilt and shame. One of the guards called him and told him to go into the visitors room, and he came in, and sat down, without even looking at me.

He looked nervous and sat forward with shoulders bunched and hands wrapped firmly round his knees.

He was wearing the same as he'd worn last time I'd seen him, the black polo neck, jeans and navy jacket and his face was clean shaven and hair newly brushed straight back. He was obviously ready for the visit, and I thought back to Phil's comment in the car about it not mattering if I didn't get there.

His voice was weaker than before and it shook as he spoke and I wondered what was up. "It's you again . . . I thought you came back."

"Ian, why is she late?", the guard suddenly demanded in a loud voice. He spoke slowly emphasising every syllable in the way you might speak to someone who was deaf or so idiotic they couldn't understand you. Ian didn't answer him but kept his head bowed.

"You know the visiting hours. Why didn't you tell her?", he demanded.

I watched in amazement. Why couldn't the guard ask me those questions? Why was he shouting at Ian, because I'd failed to turn up at the specified time? "My train was late", I whispered towards Ian, conspiratorally.

"Her train was late", he repeated to the guard in a monotone voice and glanced up at me. The guard went on and on and on about rules and regulations that must be obeyed, but not to me; just to Ian. In a voice that barked like a sergeant major and yet all in that manner, the manner of someone talking to someone who is deaf. Deaf or stupid.

And I just sat there.

Thinking back now to that day, I'd wished I had stood up and said something, or even asked politely why he was doing it. But then, to my shame, I just sat there and thought of myself and the trouble I was in, and felt a burning resentment towards Ian as if it was somehow his fault.

The whole scene in front of me reminded me of a song by Bob Dylan, where it says - *"and so they took him to the jailhouse where, they try to turn a man into a mouse"* - This reminded me of the song.

It always said in newspapers of his stereo record player, and his hotel like room, and Christmas dinner, and yet the Christmas dinner was a school dinner, the record player a battered scratchy cheap old one, the bed a spartan single mattress and the room the size of a toilet.

For company, guards and insane old men, who hated him, and took pleasure in tormenting him, and at best, ignoring him. His solace and comfort only the retreat into his head where memories of blood covered walls in council houses and screams of his victims chased him out of his own tortured mind to the sole retreat of countless and endless medications that he couldn't live without.

I watched as he pulled out one of his cigarettes and as his hands fumbled with the matches, large bony fingers trembling so much he could barely light up.
I looked at him. How could I tell him about the trouble I was in? How could I say I was terrified in case he confirmed that I was his daughter.

I thought of saying it, and then realised that I couldn't? How much could one man take. How on their own could one man stand?

I asked him did he get lonely, then as soon as I'd said it, wished I hadn't.

He kept his gaze to the floor and didn't answer, just drew heavily on his cigarette then looked up at me, an expression of anger in his eyes.

I didn't know what he'd expected of me. Was I supposed to care for him, to feel compassion or sympathy for his isolation.

I thought back to when I'd first written to him. She cared, the girl that had written to him then, but that wasn't me. She was crazy, she was stupid and had strange ideas, and she'd got me into the trouble I was in now.
It was all his own fault, and now he was suffering and I was expected to watch it.

The air hung with depression, sadness, regrets, and pain. I had to get out of there! it was like watching someone being crucified, and not being able to help or like watching someone in the confines of their personal hell.

I slipped my thumb into the front of my jeans, the birth certificate was still there, and the idea of handing it to him seemed absurd. I opened my mouth to try to explain, somehow what had happened and to ask him whether he had any idea what I should do. Just at that moment a guard walked in and announced time was up.

I turned and moved out towards the door, and he followed me. I automatically gave my hand as he offered out his, and then as he held it, and surrounded by the guard waiting to take him back to his room, he squeezed it, just for a second, really tight, and I looked up surprised and he smiled or sort of smiled, but his mouth didn't turn up at the corners, just straightened out so it didn't really make a proper smile. I remember wondering whether he'd forgotten how to smile . . . I had come to find out once and for all. "Did you know Mary Sweeney? Did you know her some nine months before I was born? Ian Stewart Brady. Am I your daughter? . . . The papers would crucify both me and him if his answer was yes!

And then it was for the second time that I found myself walking through the swing doors and being escorted by a guard out to the security gate at the end of the path.

I made my way out to the waiting car outside the gates, and pulled a face at Phil when he jumped on me straight away to find out what had happened.

"Can I talk about it later?", I snapped. I was tired and exhausted and the lack of sleep was beginning to take it's toll.

The journalist from Manchester made me pose for some photos outside the hospital and I was getting more and more annoyed as he made me walk-up and down, again and again, so that he could get a decent shot.

We finished up, and drove back to Manchester airport and caught the flight back to London Heathrow.
By the time we reached London I was fit to drop and Phil kept on and on trying to find out Ian's reaction to me showing him my birth certificate.

I couldn't work out what to say, and I wanted time to make up some sort of story. We got back to the hotel, and I shut myself in my room and flung myself on the bed.

Every nerve in my body seemed taut with tension and nerves; I had to think of something to say before Phil came back.

I lay there thinking desperately and then came to the conclusion that I'd have to lie. I'm a bad liar at the best of times but it had to work; my life being ruined depended on it. I had to stop them from doing their story. The door opened and I looked up expecting to see Phil but instead it was Ted Hynds. My heart sank; of the two he was the toughest. He'd be virtually impossible to lie to.

I sat up on the bed and started trying to answer his questions, as to what had happened when I'd visited Ian Brady. I told him of how I'd shown him the birth certificate and he'd replied "Why are you showing me this? I've never been near Hull in my life, and I certainly don't know of any Mary or of any love child."

I looked up to see Ted's reaction, and to my surprise he sat there grinning."You're not very good at it you know." I looked at him wide-eyed, "What do you mean?."

He opened his eyes to their full capacity, fluttered his eyelashes innocently and mocked in a high pitched girl's voice "What do you mean?", then laughed his usual deep throated chuckle.

"You had five minutes in there, barely enough time to say hello. Now, did you show him the birth certificate or not?"

"No", I said timidly, knowing that it would annoy him.

I was right.

"You didn't go all the way there at our expense just to chat about the weather."

I blushed and looked away, "I'm sorry, but it seemed a bit ridiculous, especially as I know he's not my father. Anyway there's no story now is there."

Ted glanced at me in an expression of surprise."You're on television advertising the Sunday People and your story, after Blind Date, and then every two hours in the commercial breaks until eleven thirty."

Phil came in and I ignored him and stared in disbelief at Ted. "I'm what!"

"You're on T.V. It's our week for advertising so we'll show the best photograph of you, then flash up Brady to give a hint of the story."

My stomach churned, "What story?, there is no story."

"Of course there is, it's already written. The Devil's Daughter is the headline and it's a splash", Ted announced proudly, a big smile on his face.

"The Devil's what?" I half shouted.

"The Devil's Daughter, Ted's a big Dennis Wheatley fan", said Phil grinning. "You can't say that, it's not a joke, it's my life, and if it's going to be on television everyone's going to see it. My foster parents will see it, my father's got a weak heart."

"Everybody's going to see it anyway", Phil said snappily.

I looked at them in disbelief. It seemed as if I for all the world wasn't a person but the subject of a story, and as the subject of a story I was worthless, a non-person, and nothing mattered apart from getting the most sensational coverage. I was learning very quickly .

With that the woman journalist came in and I stood up and went over to her and tried to plead with her. She was a woman, she'd know how I felt. "They are

138

going to say he's my father and I can't stop them", I said and started to cry again.

"It's okay, she's just a bit nervous", Phil said.

The woman journalist patted me on the shoulder. "It's okay, don't worry about anything, Phil and Ted are looking after you."

"But I don't want the story done, it will ruin my life. How would you feel if you were me?" I asked her.

"I wouldn't write or visit Ian Brady for a million pounds", she snapped and turned her back towards me.

I sat back down. So that was it! They didn't treat everyone like this. It was because it was all about Ian Brady, the Moors Murderer . . . the one they referred to as the Devil incarnate . . .
I should have known.

Hated by everyone, he stood alone and was trusted by no-one. Who could blame him? I thought of Alan who I had trusted. He thought he was justified in what he had done because of what I had done, something that no-one approved of. I'd stretched out a hand towards Ian Brady - and in doing that I'd stepped over some sort of line, some sort of boundary beyond the accepted perimeters.

I thought back to the nights in the orphanage where I'd felt so akin to him, in some sort of way and I knew that it was too late to cry. Too late to try and stop it. It had already been done. It had already been done years ago and it had all somehow led up to this. And now it was him and me. To the readers of the People, and to the T.V. audiences, I was already condemned and it was too late to try to deny it.
I belonged over the line. It was my territory even though I knew little of it. And I couldn't have stopped any of this happening.

And I was sitting there thinking this, and all of a sudden I got a feeling within me, like the girl who had first written to Ian, the one that believed in something even though she wasn't sure what it was. And I felt a power rise within me, like a kind of strength, a kind of feeling that nothing could hurt me or touch me. Like an invincibility. And it was the first time that I got that feeling, the feeling I began to get whenever I acted on a sort of compulsion within me, whenever I ignored my own reasoning and let my compulsion do the leading for me.

I don't remember much about what happened next. The following day was Saturday and I spent it alone in the hotel room. Not daring to turn the television on in case I saw the advertisement flash up when I least expected it. ... Not daring to see my picture in the middle of the newspaper's sensational exposure. I hadn't slept much except half an hour here and there, and when I did I dreamt of people chasing me and beating me over the head with clubs, and headlines on newspaper stories, my face covered in warts and looking hideous and shining out from the front cover of every newspaper on every newspaper stand. 'This girl is Ian Brady's Daughter, and I'd wake up sweating and looking round the hotel room and wondering where the hell I was.

Sunday morning the day of the story and I felt nauseous and dizzy. The whole situation seemed so unreal and frightened me so much. I felt disconnected and lost as if my whole world was going off balance or had somehow been pulled out at the roots.

The phone started buzzing and startled me, and I picked it up and it was Ted, bright, breezy and excited.

"Have you seen it yet?", he asked.
I went hot and cold; then numb. Today was the day! Today was the day everyone who went to a newsagents would be greeted by a large photograph of me and then the headline. 'The Devil's Daughter'. I thought back to all the people I had known way back in the past, and the people I'd been to school

140

with. I wondered what they'd think of me, what my parents would think when they went to pick up the paper after Church on Sunday.

"I haven't seen it Ted", I whispered. "I don't want to, I couldn't take it, I'm too scared."

"Why, why?", said Ted cheerily, "It's a very good story, and you'll be pleased to know they didn't use my headline, The Devil's Daughter."

"Didn't they?", I said tentatively relieved that at least I had been spared that.

"No, so there's nothing to worry about. You'll like it, you really will. Look, you stay there and I'll ring room service and I'll get them to send up a copy."

I was on tenterhooks until I heard a soft knock on the door, then a girl's voice, "Your newspaper." I went and took it off her and shut the door again. Then sat on the bed and unfolded the paper. There it was, my face, me, covering half the front page of the newspaper. It looked strange and stupid, not like a real paper, but a toy town paper that somebody had had printed up as a joke.

And then the headline, underneath the huge photo, the photo of me taken when I was drunk, smiling and looking like a demented tart with bright red lipstick - smiling next to a headline like that, 'I Am Brady's Daughter'. I looked half insane, only someone crazy would smile and say something like that so proudly and ignorantly, unaware of the pain it may cause. The pain it would cause to the parents of people he had killed. The story looked grotesque, and was grotesque, but there it was, my face, my name, my story . . . . I wanted to scream.

I flung it down on the bed and picked up the phone and dialled Ted's room number. I remember screaming at him, swearing, sobbing and shouting all at the same time. He'd ruined my life! And it was over, and that bastard sat there celebrating his front page scoop.

I couldn't hear him answer on the phone, and I let it fall and ran out into the corridor and started banging and kicking on his door. It was flung open and I was shocked to see it was the woman journalist in Phil's room. She came out into the corridor and leant forward at me and slapped me hard across the face and told me to calm down. I lunged back at her and she squared up to me, "Don't you dare love, you're no match to me." I backed down. I'd always had a kind of fear of physical violence.

I put my hand to my cheek, she caught it with her nail and I looked at my hand and saw that it was bleeding. Phil came out of his room and helped me inside and Ted, who had come out of his room because of the noise, followed us in too. I sat on the bed totally numb and shaking and trying to catch my breath and I hiccuped in huge mouthfuls of air. And they stared at me, as if I was hysterical for no reason.

Ted poured me a vodka from one of the miniatures in the fridge and mixed it with a bottle of tonic, then handed it to me.

"I know it's breakfast time, but it'll calm you."

I gulped it down, and leant forward and sobbed, holding my head in my hands.

"The story was so stupid, I looked so stupid, smiling like that and saying things like 'I thought he'd make a wonderful father'."

I looked around at them, "Which one of you made that up ? Don't you think it's in bad taste, but it's okay, not to worry", I said sarcastically, "Because it's my face there, my name and it's down as something I said, so it's all okay, isn't it?"

I made a run for the door, I couldn't seem to breathe in that room and Ted grabbed me, "You're hysterical, calm down."

I looked at my face in the mirror. I had a large scratch down the side of it that bled slightly, and my make up was smeared all over my face.

I felt an incredible sense of panic and fear; it was like I knew everyone outside would be reading it, and yet I was desperately dependent on the people in the room for my safety and yet they were the ones who had written it. And they frightened me with their cynicism and their ruthlessness and the way they treated me like someone different from them.

I did then what I felt I only had one choice to do. I threw myself on their mercy and tried to appeal to their sense of pity.

"Look, I'm sorry for the way I behaved, I'm just really scared", I said quietly.

Phil leant down and took my hand, "What is it that you're so scared of?"

"People hating me", I sobbed. "They'll be trying to kill me, and I'll have nowhere to go, no-one to turn to."

"Look, you're being over dramatic, but if it makes you feel any better we'll take you out of the country for a week, while we're writing up the second part to go in next week."

I gulped back the rest of the drink I was still holding.

"Yes, yes, that sounds good. Somewhere miles away, somewhere where they don't read the Sunday People."

They waited until Monday morning and Phil took me to get a passport. Then in the afternoon we packed up our stuff and drove down to Dover.

The woman journalist had left us by then, and I was left alone with Phil and Ted. We stopped off at a pub for a quick lunch on the drive down to Dover and sipped lagers and ate ploughmans lunches, and the tension between us began to ease.

It was about two o'clock and grey and miserable when we drove the car into the ferry and went upstairs and tried to find ourselves comfortable seats.

We mostly dozed on the ferry and as Phil slept I picked up the magazine he was reading, 'Private Eye', the satirical review, and I started to read the articles he had turned to.

"Look at this", I said loudly and woke Phil from his dozing. "It says here, Emma Ridley, the wild child, did a deal with the News of the World for fourteen thousand pounds for the story of her marriage."
I looked at Phil, who was rubbing the sleep out of his eyes. "I didn't know you got paid for stories."

Phil and Ted shot a quick glance across to each other and I wondered what was up.

"Famous people sell stories, not ordinary members of the public, who are no-one, if that's what you're thinking", he laughed, then looked over quickly at Ted.

"Oh sorry, I just wondered. I didn't think she was very famous though, that girl."

Ted looked at me angrily, "People are greedy and stupid, that's the problem." They both seemed to be suddenly in a bad mood and I thought that I must have jolted a bad memory or something, so I quickly changed the subject.

Ted though was mostly in high spirits, he kept laughing out loud and slapping

144

his knee. His bosses had said only Phil was to take me out of the country, but Ted had got on the phone and told them that I'd demanded to be minded by two journalists, and he was busy pulling out maps and planning what we'd do.

"Right, we'll drive through to the South of France towards the sun", he said excitedly. Phil seemed less eager. "No I think we'd better stay near the ferry in Boulogne in case we're needed.

Ted looked at me, "Phil's a bit of a bore, but never mind, we'll try not to let him spoil it for us."

I laughed back at Ted and warmed to him. He'd seemed to have changed all of a sudden, from a hard businessman into a small kid, full of fun and mischief.

Later on during the ferry crossing I fell asleep in the chair next to Phil and woke up to find his seat empty. I went for a walk to try to find him and eventually did so on the upper deck sipping red wine and laughing to himself.

"I don't believe I managed to swing it", he laughed. "A week in The South of France, just what I need. Big hand is on my side as always."

"Who's big hand?", I said as I looked at him curiously.

"Big hand, that's God, silly", he laughed.

And again I was amazed at the change in him, he seemed like someone completely different. Gone was the businessman, and in his place, the schoolboy, and he seemed like a lot of fun.

He ordered a glass of red wine for me and some cheese, as we sat on deck looking at the French Coastline, and I forgot myself for a while and relaxed slightly.

To get out of the Country was a perfect idea. England. The newspaper story. I wanted to distance myself from it as far as I could, even though it was temporary, I couldn't tolerate the fear inside me, and I wanted it to lessen, to leave me for a while, allowing me to sleep; to stop the endless crying.

I looked at Ted, "I want to see the sun, I want to see the sun and I know when I see it I won't be scared anymore." And I let tears flow down my face unchecked. And Ted looked at me in surprise.
"Come on now, no more tears", he said kindly, "Forget it for a while and take a rest. It's a holiday now."

"On my own practically though", I sniffed. "It's not like with friends."

"Er pardon", he said playfully, "You're with your uncle Ted and you're going to have fun, because I'm going to make sure of it."

I glanced at him, to see if he meant it, and he winked at me just like an uncle would have done, and threw his arm round my shoulder and squeezed me.
We finished off the wine and cheese, then walked slowly back to where Phil was still sleeping, and laughed at him as he slumped there snoring with his mouth hanging open.

When we finally reached France and re-boarded the car, we headed south straight away. Phil took the wheel of the steel blue Rover, that was his usual company car; I sat up beside him while Ted fell across the back seat. Phil and I kept turning to look at him and marvelling at how innocent he looked when he was asleep, hair defying gravity, an angelic, peaceful, expression on his face.

The only cassettes Phil had taken in his car were Simply Red and Genesis and they were played over and over again. Invisible Touch and Throwing It All Away as we sped across France. The speedometer reading a constant hundred miles an hour, and it was about after two and a half hours or so that we parked

146

up in front of a roadway refreshment stand and we all swopped seats, with Ted this time taking the wheel, with Phil up beside him while I lay across the back seat.

What seemed like ages later, and after dreams of everybody I ever knew coming towards me with rolled up newspapers, an expression of hatred on their faces, I awoke. The first thing I heard was raucous laughter and the radio playing loudly, and I poked my head between the two front seats to see both of my escorts driving along in their swimming trunks; Ted had just finished devouring a choc ice and he was busy licking the paper wrapper clean, when I noticed the sun at a burning temperature and my throat was parched dry.

They turned and saw I had awoken and I sat up and watched them and laughed. "You two are supposed to be professional businessmen, minding me, not large school kids on an outing, driving along in your under garments and licking chocolate wrappers and stuffing ice-creams all the way."

"We're your foster parents for the week, and you are our little girl", intoned Ted. "Now do as little girls are supposed to do, and be seen and not heard."

I smiled at him, and sat back in the seat and looked out the window. The sun was burning hot as it shone through the glass on my face and the scenery outside looked beautiful, all sort of vineyards and dusty roads.

It was about half an hour after I'd woken up when we came to what Ted had been looking for. It was along a hidden tree lined avenue, and then you turned into a gateway and there it was, Pont du Gard.

And there it stood, an enormous towering bridge, like something they blew up on 'A Bridge Too Far", (as Ted kept telling us over and over again).

The river was a deep blue colour and, built on the side of a small hill nearly on the river, our hotel, a secluded and hidden French peasant manor type place, like a castle almost, with huge grey stones and a marble floored outdoor restaurant looking over to a beautiful view beyond the bridge.

My room, opposite Ted's, was beautiful. A double room done out in a peasant house style with a dark wooden bed and a white old fashioned bathroom.

The weather was burning hot, and a mosquito net covered the window. There were huge wooden shutters in case you wanted to block out the sun that shone into the room every morning.

I picked up the pale porcelain phone and dialled room service and ordered some freshly ground coffee, and it was beautiful, better than anything I had ever tasted. After that I ordered it every morning, and it was blissful to wake up around midday after a luxurious sleep and stretch in the crisp white cool cotton sheets, open the shutters and look out to that bridge and the burning South of France sun. Coffee and warm croissants, then I'd make my way out to the terrace to meet Ted who normally sat at one of the white tables like a real old English gentleman, dressed in white and reading The Times. He had that lovely upper class public school boy accent and he'd quote poetry all the time, and by about two o'clock invariably drunk too much.

Most of the time we'd spend the afternoons sunbathing together, then have swimming races out to the rocks in the middle of the river and back again.

In the evenings, Ted would pick a restaurant from the Michelin guide and we'd drive out to different places like Egremont, a small, very old, half ruined city with fountains and old churches, so it looked like somewhere in Rome.
We'd sit at an outdoor restaurant in the fading evening sun, our skins still reddened and hot from the rays, and we'd sip chilled Chablis and eat moules marinieres with our fingers, and talk and laugh for hours and hours.

Ted would get more and more drunk as the evening wore on, and would get funnier and funnier, recounting stories of things he'd got up to while he was on various assignments.

Phil was quieter, and with his grey beard and steel rimmed glasses and air of seriousness, he drew my attention a lot with his reticence. I'd never met anyone like him before, studious and intelligent. The usual men I'd come into contact with would be like David or my foster father, working class men happiest down the pub with their friends on a Friday and Saturday night, the only conversation about their cars or football or the jobs they did.

The alcohol would usually make Ted emotional when he'd got past his second bottle of wine, and he'd start talking emotionally about his son Edward, a small sandy haired little boy who spent most of his time at boarding school. We'd stopped at Ted's house before we left for Dover for him to pack a suitcase. He lived with his mother in Richmond, after his wife deserted him, and his small son while the boy was on holiday from boarding school. Seeing both of them together reminded me of that film with Richard Harris where he goes on that mission with Richard Burton and leaves the small boy at boarding school . . . . 'The Wild Geese.'

Ted was very attractive, and although I wasn't sexually attracted to him I could see how a lot of women could be.

He was very charming and good company and I practically purred after spending an evening conversing with him over dinner with the candlelight and the wine.

After dinner the three of us, usually heady from the wine, used to link arms with me in the middle and walk round from our hotel over the bridge, and over to the other side of the river and to the campsite buried in the trees opposite the hotel.

We'd walk along in the dark, singing and laughing and holding each other up.

Then when we'd get to the camp site we'd buy huge glasses of that lovely champagne brandy that you can lug back from their log cabin bar, and we'd sit outside in the dark listening to the crickets and talking, and drinking ourselves into oblivion; each of us revelling in the freedom, the booze helping to cast our not inconsiderable problems to one side, if only for a while.

The days flew by and soon a week had passed, and we received orders from the editor that we'd have to come back. We all sat on the balcony in the hotel restaurant and drank champagne 'kirs'. Ted had been drinking most of the day and the 'kirs' only helped to worsen his condition. Phil seemed strangely sad and still seemed depressed by the time we reached the restaurant, and we sat on the white painted wooden veranda and drank a heavy burgundy wine that Ted had chosen, and ruminated on the fact that the week had come to an end and we'd be heading back for England the next day. The recollection that my foster parents had to be faced along with everybody else, as the newspaper article flashed into my mind with cruel clarity, and I pushed it away and looked at the surroundings. Two white horses were tied to posts on the veranda and the two men who owned them sat drinking with their dark weather beaten faces and gap toothed grins. Phil explained that they made their living from capturing the wild horses, taming them and then selling them. It seemed to be an awful, cruel way to make money and I sat watching the two men in disapproval, hoping they'd notice my resentful stare.

None of us were very talkative that evening. The sun had burnt my face and it stung whenever I opened my mouth, and it felt dry and sore.

I watched Phil as he conversed with Ted, his grey hair made him look more intelligent than he was and the glasses adding to his air of an intellectual.

He was discussing politics and I started to stare, and then found myself wondering what sort of girlfriend he had and if someone like me would ever have a chance with him. When he suddenly stopped what he was saying and turned and caught me staring, I blushed and turned away. Then he reached out and pulled out one of the yellow roses in the vase on the table and handed it to me, "A yellow rose to match your hair", he said softly.

Ted looked at him an amazed look on his face, "Phil's got a crush on you, haven't you Phil?", he asked mockingly.

My face went even redder and I bent my head down and stared at the tiny yellow rosebud he had handed me.

After dinner we all linked arms again and went from bar to bar in the little french village ordering brandy after brandy, and drinking it back in one go.

The sun was still up and cast a watery gold glow over everything and I tried to put it out of my mind that this was all over now and I'd soon be back in England to face the pain again.

As we drove back to the hotel, after it turned dark, we drove down a long tree lined dust track. There was a full moon and it shone through the tops of the trees making them appear silver, and lit up the sides of the road so the yellow grass had a kind of golden glow. Phil slowed up, then stopped the car and turned off the headlights and we sat in the dark. With the heat and the windows open and the sound of crickets outside on the grass it was like being in Africa or somewhere very hot.

I heard a faint snore and Phil and I turned to see Ted fast asleep in the back of the car.

"It's romantic isn't it?' Phil asked as he turned around to study the view.
I could see him watching me from out of the corner of my eye.

"I'd like to kiss you, but I suppose it's out of the question", he half whispered.

I sat there, my face growing hotter again until he turned the engine back on and we drove slowly back to the hotel. I hadn't answered his question. The moment passed.

We got back to the hotel in about half an hour then bid each other goodnight and went to our separate rooms.

I'd just got undressed when I heard a knock, so I pulled a towel around me and pulled the door ajar. It was Phil "I have to speak to you", his tone sounded urgent and I thought something was up, so I opened the door and stood back. As soon as he got in he pulled me down on the bed, "You must know how I feel about you."

He started kissing the back of my neck, hands pinning back my arms so I couldn't push him away. . . . The towel leaped away and his gaze on my nakedness embarrassed me . . . I wanted him . . . and I didn't want him . . . I struggled free and stood up "Look I'm engaged, so are you." I reached for the towel to hide what his stare was devouring.

"But I'm in love with you", he croaked as he slipped out of his shirt, then moved towards me again. His body was bronzed from the sun, and the scent from his aftershave made me quite heady. He pulled me to him roughly pressing his mouth against my neck. Just for a moment I felt a strong need inside me, and then my senses returned and I pushed him away with all the strength I could muster and picked up his shirt and stuffed it in his hands. Suddenly, I was furious with him. This man was supposed to be protecting me, not seducing me!

"Get out or I'll call Ted", I screamed, feeling humiliated.

"But I don't want just this. I don't just want one night. I want it to be more than that."

"Well it won't be just one night." I said incredulously. "You're not having one night, or one bloody minute. It's no, Phil . . . leave me alone. I don't want you."

He stood back and looked at me. "You know how you feel about me, and I feel it too" he began. "Alright then, we'll take it slowly and I'll prove to you I'm not that sort of guy that you think I am. We'll go out to dinner as soon as we get back to England, and I'll woo you slowly with wine and roses.

"We've had the wine and roses, and it doesn't make any difference, I've only ever slept with one man so far and I never married him. The next man I sleep with will be my husband, wine and roses won't matter. I don't care if he's living on the street dirt poor or looks like the hunchback of Notredame. If he's my hero, then I'll give myself to him." I stopped and looked at him and he put his shirt on and left.

I woke in the night to hear further knocking at the door but lay there in the dark and waited for it to stop. My head was straight, perhaps for the first time in a long time, I felt strong and resourceful. Phil's attempted seduction had somehow strengthened my resolve.

The next morning he wouldn't meet my eyes over breakfast and Ted kept looking from one to the other of us curiously wondering what the strained atmosphere was all about.

We packed up that day and loaded the car with our cases and I slept in the back as we drove North to the ferry that would take us back to England.

When I awoke, I didn't sleep in the car, I just watched out the window until the bright sunlight became weaker and weaker and eventually gave way to a grey gloominess and I felt a growing sinking feeling and depression inside, coupled with a kind of fear of what lay ahead.

On the ferry, I slept for what seemed like hours and then when I awoke we were already back in England, and it was like waking up to a nightmare.

Phil was out on deck and Ted sat next to me penning a letter. I sat watching him for a while, and I was just about to say something when I noticed something about him; he seemed to have an air of coldness around him as if the Ted I had come to know in the Pont du Gard had been some other person and now the old person had returned, the one I had first met, the businessman; the one I had been afraid of.

I sat watching him for a long time, mourning the absence of the warm friend I had come to know and like so much, and telling myself that I was imagining things due to too much wine the night before; and then he looked up at me and I saw it all in his eyes; icy with indifference, almost a stranger and I felt the cold close in when a man's voice on the speaker announced that we were just about to dock at Dover.

We left the ferry and drove from Dover up through to Richmond.

Ted insisted that I phone my foster parents to tell them I was coming home.

They dropped me at a call box, and sat in the car and waited while I made the phone call.

They hung up, as soon as I said my name and I re-dialled, this time my father's voice, "We gave you a chance, and you've proved you were what we thought you were. Your stuff has been thrown out, and if you call here again, we'll phone the police. You've dragged our name through the mud, and it's not even yours to do it with." He hung up. And I hung up. And I walked back to the waiting car.

The reaction I got wasn't what I expected, not from the two friends I'd known on holiday. "What are we supposed to do with you?" Phil started, "The story's over, it's into print tomorrow, there's no need for us to keep you anymore . . . ."

My stomach churned. I couldn't believe what I was hearing. I felt used and then dropped.

Phil put the car into gear irritably and drove off. Our first stop was Richmond and Ted's house. The journey was carried out in virtual silence. When we arrived, Ted got out and so did Phil and I watched them as they stood talking conspiratorially.

I heard Ted say, "This is for you", as he handed Phil a bottle of brandy he'd picked up from duty free and then he turned, walked towards his house without so much as an acknowledgement to my existence.

Phil got in and started the car. We'd driven about a mile and I leant over the seat, "Is Ted meeting us later?."

"Don't be silly", Phil laughed, "You'll probably never see him again."

I opened my mouth to say, "But that can't be true, because he didn't say goodbye", but I closed it again as I looked at Phil's back, cold, hard, driving the car in a professional way. And I realised I'd been wrong when I'd jokingly accused them of not being professional when they'd been enjoying themselves. They were certainly professional at pretending and feigning friendship, but why, why pretend when I'd already told them everything I knew?

Phil drove into London and headed for the Earl's Court area. "Earl's Court has plenty of cheap bed and breakfast places and I'll pay out of my own money for the first night for you. Ted should, by rights, he's the one that's done well out of you, it doesn't matter to me what they pay him; I'm not the freelance, he is."

"What do you mean?", I started, "They don't give money for stories, especially ones about Ian Brady, Why should I get paid? I didn't want the story to go ahead anyway!"

"Someone with a head on their shoulders would have cleaned up with that story, ten thousand at the minimum, and you made a fool of yourself for nothing!"

"I had no choice", I started.

"Yes, but you shouldn't have been so gullible, Ted kept laughing about you believing things he was telling you, and I kept sticking up for you saying she's not as stupid as she looks, but he was right . . . . You are! . . . You've lost your home, your parents, friends, and all for what? . . . sod all! . . . "

He stopped the car in front of a small bed and breakfast, and helped me in with my case, and then up to the the small single room, he'd rented for me.

The room was even worse than the outside! Peeling yellowed wallpaper, the stink of stale sweat and a single bed with a paper thin mattress and eggshell blue nylon sheets.

"This is what we do to people", Phil said thoughtfully as he walked up and down the room,
"The press are so powerful, the media so powerful, do you know? Can you imagine how many people's lives we affect every week?"
I looked up at him. I was a statistic, even there sitting in front of him, a nonperson, like I'd been before.

He sat down on the bed next to me and handed me his work phone number.

"If you're keeping in contact with Brady, we'll find out about it, so you may as well keep me informed."

I'd forgotten all about <u>him</u> with all the fuss, and the memory of his face flickered up in my mind. I wondered what he thought of the story, a story that someone thought they were his daughter, and me, me, who he'd seemed not to have wanted to say goodbye to. It was all out now. The guards would have shown the newspaper to Ian. I wouldn't need to ask about him and Mary . . .

"There won't be any contact with him, I've learned my lesson. I'm like everyone else, I don't want to be different, I'm not strong enough to go through all this. Not again, never again."

He reached up and put his arm round me, "Look, there's no way I can get involved with someone like you, you're linked with the lowest of the low, but to show I don't even judge you on that, I still want to kiss you."

I stood up and wiped away tears that had started running down my face so he couldn't see them. He moved towards me. I allowed his arms around me and his lips on mine, until I realised that this was no kiss of sympathy or farewell. His tongue sought mine - it was then that I shoved him away.

I couldn't hate him; he was just a businessman doing a job, and the smooth talking seemed to be a part of it. It was like he didn't realise how he was hurting me.

He got up, moved towards the door and opened it and cast a last long look around the room, then at me.

The tears now were flowing and I was past caring that he could see. I sat back down on the edge of the bed, feeling hopeless, and totally forlorn.

"Be strong", he said softly. I heard the door click. I looked up and he had gone.

I lay there for a while, then undressed and got into the strange bed. Incredibly, I slept deeply all night, then woke next morning at ten o'clock to the cruel morning light shining through the dusty window. I felt cut off from everything normal . . . Alienated . . . Outside and alone.

First thing and I went for something to eat, then I left the small bed and breakfast into the seedy side of the Earls Court area, and walked along to the nearest newsagents to buy a copy of The Sunday People and some sandwiches. I walked slowly back to the room chewing the sandwiches disinterestedly and flicking through the paper to see where I was. I couldn't find it, so I waited till I got back in the room and looked again and there it was filling the centre pages, 'Brady Sobs Goodbye' and a large picture of me in the awful tarty clothes and the red lipstick and my hair in curls, the way it never should have been. None of it.

The photograph was out of place and the story so unreal it made me feel stupid and cheap. And I lay back on the bed and sobbed.

The crying went on for so long that I felt weak and helpless and needed someone to talk to.

I grabbed some change from my purse and went down to the pay phone in the foyer and dialled David's mother's number. David had had his phone cut off and he was close to his mother so we normally passed messages through her on a daily basis.

I was looking forward to pouring my heart out to her, she was a woman, she'd understand. I was sobbing by the time I got though to her, the voice was cold and harsh on the other end, "I don't want you near my son again. David was round here the other night. He's gone now up to Scotland to stay with friends till all this blows over, and he told me he never wants to see your face again. He just feels lucky he knew all this before the marriage -"

I hung up and sobbed bitterly leaning my head against the wall.

I replaced the receiver and I began to feel real fear inside. David had been my friend, my lover, the only one who really cared.

No-one would speak to me. I was starting to feel a panicky breathless feeling and I dialled the number of my best friend, Maya. She gasped as she heard my voice at the other end, "I didn't think you would phone. Do you realise what sort of trouble you're in?."

I choked on the sobs, "No, no I don't, I didn't realise till I started phoning people, what trouble, what trouble?."

"Look my mum's come in, I've got to go."
"Can I phone you later?", I half screamed, there was a click and she was gone.

I felt numb inside as if my whole world was rocking and slipping away from me.

I dialled the number Phil had given me on the business card and a male voice answered and said "Newsdesk."
"Is Phil Hall there, I have to speak to him!" They wouldn't give out his number but they promised to phone him and get him to phone me. I hung up and sat, shaking, by the phone. There was no ring but strange clicks so I picked it up and heard Phil's voice at the other end. Thank God, someone who wouldn't be shocked to hear my voice, it was making me panic.

I sobbed down the phone that no-one would speak to me, and he sounded tired and irritable as he answered. "Look I'm busy, really, but look I tell you what I'll do; there's a letter at the Sunday People offices for you, from Ian Brady, I'll pop it over tomorrow."

He told me he couldn't talk further and despite my protests hung up.

I don't think I have ever felt so desperately alone and sick with fear in all my life.

Everything swam and tilted in front of me as if my very world was rocking and rocking and I was just about to slip off.

I went back to the room and laid on the bed, and cried some more and then finally, fell into a fitful sleep. The dreams, nightmares really, were there again.

I woke early the next day after a night sleeping off and on and crying and re-reading the newspaper story.

I watched the clock then waited till nine o'clock. It was Monday and I'd have to tell work that I'd be in the following day to give me a chance to look for somewhere to live. The receptionist Gillian with whom I always shared a joke sounded shocked to hear me, and then put me through to Steve, my boss, without a word.

Steve was very apologetic about it but he said he had to do it, and I couldn't believe my ears.

"You were on the front pages of a national newspaper saying you were an employee of a West London Detective Agency. I just don't want any links here with someone like Ian Brady, it's bad for business and I could lose clients over this. I'm sorry, I'll have to let you go. If you tell me where you are I'll pay you up till the end of the month.

I gave him the address of the bed and breakfast and hung up.

I spent the day looking around the area for a bedsitting room and had no luck, when I told them I was currently unemployed.

I came back to the bed and breakfast at about seven o'clock and I paid the woman for an extra two nights. She handed me over a letter in a long brown envelope with a note attached to it and I brought it upstairs with me to the room.

It was strange really reading that letter, after everyone reacting so horribly to me. Here was someone acting friendly, and it was Ian Brady.

The note attached was from Phil. "I opened it by mistake, we are running a story on it."

I couldn't believe it, not again.

I scanned through the letter to see what it was they could possibly do a story on, and I saw it, and I could hardly believe it.

And I read the words with a growing horror inside "I remember your mother. Of course to prove you were mine there would have to be a blood test."

I folded the letter and ran downstairs and phoned Phil's newsdesk and got them to call me back.

"You can't", I started, before he had a chance to say anything.

Phil started to laugh, "He believes he's your father, it's unbelievable isn't it?"

"It's the way you wrote that stupid story, you know I wasn't certain."

"Never mind, what's important is he admits to having a long lost daughter."

"That's cruel, that's really cruel, what if he's always wanted a family?"

"He's an evil monster, he's never loved anything in his life, he's incapable of

161

all feeling. It's a good story and it'll go in next Sunday under the heading "Brady admits he's her father", we've already got plenty of photos of you, so we don't need you for anything."

"Phil, you can't! Please Phil. Think of me, of my life. You're drowning me. If the bed and breakfast people see your report, they'll send me packing. Phil, please; I'll have nowhere to live, and nobody to turn to."

"They won't, don't be silly, just concentrate on yourself, don't worry about others, now what are you going to say to Brady in a reply?"

"I'm not replying ", I said quietly, "The letter's going in the bin." I stuffed it in my bag in order to get rid of it later on.

I told Phil I'd phone him sometime in the future and rung off.

I had a week to find somewhere else to live before the story came out. I decided the next day to go to Ealing. I knew the area well, and it would be easier for me to find somewhere, plus I was feeling a bit lost in the strange surroundings of Earls Court, and if I couldn't speak to anyone familiar at least I could live in an area I knew to stop the peculiar hopeless feeling I kept having inside.

It was about 3.00 in the afternoon and I'd been looking at bedsits and phoning around since the morning with no luck, so I started walking slowly towards the boulevard and shopping area to get something to eat.

I was just about to cross the road and I heard someone shout out of a passing car held up by the traffic. It was two girls I'd been very close to at school, Denise and Terry. Denise had been a particularly close friend of mine and I let out a shout and gave her a huge big grin and went running towards the car.

The car was being driven by what looked like Denise's boyfriend and Terry sat in the back seat looking beautiful beside her boyfriend.

I'd just reached the car and I leant forward to hug her and just as I did she recoiled her head and spat at me. "I've got fucking kids, I've got fucking kids and you start saying that nut case is fucking great . . . Bitch!"

I stepped back, and stood there in horror, wiping the spital from my face with the back of my sleeve.

She opened up the car door and came towards me, "Did you think you were fucking clever, you looked like a stupid tart?"

I turned away from her and stood with my head down listening to a torrent of abuse then; watched her as she walked back to the car, got in and drove off.

She'd been my best friend at school and we'd cried together on the last day, that we wouldn't see each other so much, and I hadn't seen her since then, she'd moved out of the area. I hadn't seen her since just now.

My face felt sticky and smelt funny from the spital and I walked into Oliver's the sandwich bar to use their toilets and get something to eat. I needed to rest . . . I was so alone, confused, hated.
I'd just walked in the door when a group of girls who had been talking animatedly stopped as soon as they saw me. I stared at them, thinking I was imagining things and went and bought a sandwich and glanced back at them, and still they were staring.

I took a deep breath and approached the table, "Is there something wrong? I'm sorry." I started blushing deeply.

"I work at Rinaldis. You left before I came but I've seen you up there visiting Alan", explained one of them and looked at me coldly.

"Oh I see", I said and I went and sat at a nearby table with my back to them and I could hear them as I was sitting there. Laughing, sniggering and I caught bits of their conversation. "Hope she got paid a lot for it, imagine doing that", she said, "she must be mad."

And I put the sandwich down and got up and walked out, my face hot, panicking inside.

I walked through the crowds then, In Ealing everyone was out doing their shopping and I felt some sort of deep panic as if at any time someone I didn't recognise would jump out on me and start shouting at me. And I kept scanning all the faces, ready to run if I did see anybody I knew.

I felt a hand grab hold of my arm and I jumped. Maxine, a friend of a friend I knew from years ago, "Everyone's seen the paper, everyone thinks you're really sick. He's the lowest of the low."

I didn't wait to hear any more but struggled free from her grasp and ran along the high street, in and out of the crowds until I stopped in a shop doorway, breathing hard and crying. I moved out into the street and stood and held onto the railings. The whole view in front of me suddenly appeared to 'white out' as if everything I could see just blanked and I just saw the white, and I clutched onto the railings tightly to steady myself. I stood there, shaking and crying. A fairly youngish man came up behind me and tapped gently on my shoulder, and I whizzed round and cowered in fright. "Are you okay?", he said to me and his face appeared too large as he looked at me, and his voice seemed miles away and sort of echoey.

I looked at him in fear and nodded my head and turned away.

I don't know how I made it home that day. Everything had turned into something scary and I stood on the underground terrified should anyone say anything to me.

I got in and closed the door to my room and sat on the bed shaking. I think it must have been eight o'clock and I'd got into bed to try and sleep when I heard a knock on the door, and I turned in fright then thought that it must be Phil and got up to get dressed properly and answer it.

I just about stood up when the lock in the door was turned by a key outside and the door burst open and a Greek looking man stood there holding a bunch of keys. "I'm the manager here", he said as he looked me over. I pulled up the covers of the bed over me and he walked towards the centre of the room.

"Have you got a job?" he asked me and looked around the room as if he'd never seen it before. "I could fix it for you to earn a lot, working for me in my clubs." I looked up at him, "You mean a prostitute." He grinned at me, "There's no need to put it like that; you could earn a lot."

I started to cry and I lay there with my head down praying he'd go.

"I was only asking", he said in a kind of broken English and he went towards the door, and then pulled out a pen and wrote his phone number down on a piece of paper and left it on the sideboard in the room before he left.

I phoned Phil early the next day and I told him that I had to see him. He told me he couldn't make it till the evening and arranged to come over at eight o'clock.

It was nearly ten o'clock by the time I heard a knock on the door and answered it to find Phil standing there.

I sat on the bed and cried and he put his arm round me and I told him

165

everything that had happened.

"Look", he said, "I don't know why you don't go backpacking it, what else have you got to do?.."

"But I don't want to go abroad."

"It'll sort out this mess, won't it", he said and pulled me closer towards him.

"I wish I didn't have to be here, when you print that next story. It was okay in France, it seemed miles away and it didn't matter."

"Well then, see it as your chance, you're young, you should do something like that. I'm sure there's a friend you can get together with."

I told him that there wasn't, and we sat there in silence until I cried again and he put his arm around me and I could feel his mouth pressed up against my hair, moving and his breath hot against my head.

"I'm your friend, you have got me, if you go backpacking it then I expect a regular phone call off you to see what you're doing."

I looked up and smiled at him and as I did he leant down and pushed his mouth against mine in a warm, soft, sensual kiss. He looked like Kurt Russell, with grey hair; beautiful. The temptation was too great and we made love.

He stayed for a while, and we talked and sat on the edge of the bed, until he told me he had to go.

"I mean what I say, keep in touch", he said as he stood at the door and he leant forward, kissed me on the top of the head and left. The warmth and tenderness soon became stark reality.

The next day was a Wednesday, and I woke up and found myself wondering what to do. My wages had arrived in cheque form from my employer at the reception desk, and I flicked through my building society book to see how much money I had left.

The passbook told me I was in credit 300 pounds and with my wages added to it that would make seven hundred and fifty. I walked up the Earls Court Road and headed for Kensington and Chelsea; I spent the morning wandering around the shops that had goods that were too expensive for me to ever afford.

I had no idea in my mind what I was going to do and yet for the first time in a week I felt somehow relaxed and light headed and somehow strangely optimistic.

The sun was shining that day and I kept lifting up my face towards it and trying to pretend I was back in the South of France where nothing had mattered.

I think that I was just walking along when I saw it, some sort of a notice board like a sandwich board. And I stopped for some reason, and stood there staring at it. 'America - one way flights New York 100 pounds'. I read it and then I looked in the window of the shop, some sort of travel agent, and there in the window was a great big poster of the Statue of Liberty; and I was staring at it like I was kind of mesmerised, for about five minutes or so. And then it was a while again before I decided to go inside, and ask about the tickets, the one way tickets to go to New York. I don't think I'd ever even considered it before, and it's funny if someone had suggested it to me two weeks ago, I would have said no. Why go there, away from everyone? I'd be too scared. But now, well, everyone was no-one and I felt like I could get no more frightened than I was already. And I went in and bought a ticket, one way to New York City, America. The girl counted my money from behind the desk, "What about a return?" she said as looked me in the eye.

"No, it's okay, I'm never coming back", and then I paused and looked at her, "It's better there, isn't it?."

I went back to the bed and breakfast after that and booked in for another two nights.

The ticket was in two days time. I had one day left to collect my visa.

There was a long queue at the visa office and I was shaking when I was called up. What if they turned me down, then where would my stupid idea be? But it seemed I was following a road that was already mapped out for me, and the tall blonde American official smiled at me and handed my stamped passport back. "Have a nice time out there ma'am."

And I had a smile on my face as I ran down the steps of the American Embassy and went off to buy myself a new suitcase.

The next day and it was the date of the ticket. The 4th of October 1987 and my foster brother Michael's birthday.

I thought of everyone's reaction to me and thought better of signing the card so I just sent it 'with love' and left it blank.

I packed everything into the new suitcase I'd bought then called a cab to go to Heathrow Airport and sat back and waited.

It was about quarter of an hour before it arrived and the taxi driver helped me with my suitcase out to the cab.

It was a Thursday and a watery sunlight lit up Earl's Court, so it looked less seedy than it usually did; and I tried to smile and stop the feeling of fear and panic that kept riding up inside me.

The taxi passed through Hayes and I felt a sinking sadness as we passed David's house and I could see that the curtains were drawn, so he hadn't gone to Scotland like his mother had said.

I resisted an urge to tell the taxi driver to stop and go and knock on the door and ask him to hug and hold me, but I said nothing, just looked up at his window and imagined him snuggled under his duvet, round and sweet and warm, and my insides felt weak with a deep attachment to him. Tears welled up in my eyes and I blinked them down, as the taxi driver turned the radio on and my attention was taken by the music.

I went straight to the bar when I got to Heathrow Airport Terminal Three. I was terrified and my stomach felt weak and jittery; doubts about whether I was doing the right thing or not swam round my head.

"What if I got into some sort of trouble out there? There would be no-one to turn to.

I reminded myself that there was no-one here either, and at least in America I could start again, and get some sort of a job and not be afraid to walk down the street without worrying whether I'd bump into someone I knew.

And most importantly of all, there would be no more stories. I wouldn't care what they said if I was in another country; they printed that Ian admitted that he could be my father.

I downed a martini in the bar to try and settle my nerves and it made me feel worse. I tried to eat one of their cellophane wrapped sandwiches and I took one bite and nearly fetched it up.

Then I went back and forth from the bar to the toilet, bar to the toilet, and then picked up a newspaper there to try to take my mind off my fears.

169

Panicky thoughts kept forcing their way into my head, and a mocking voice kept saying, "Who do you think you are, you have never been out of the country before, you can't cope and what will you do for money?" I stood up and walked over to the flight board. My flight was due to leave in twenty minutes, but it still hadn't been called and I still hadn't weighed in my suitcase.

I went back into the toilets in the departure lounge, the air was heavy with perfume and the impersonal air of smartly dressed sophisticated women all going off to different places and meeting different people.

I turned and looked at myself in the brightly lit mirrors. I looked pale and pinched, and I felt out of my depth. What was I doing? I couldn't do this! Go to live for good in a country I didn't know anything about.

I thought in my head about someone to phone, someone to tell, and I remembered the reactions I'd got in the Earl's Court bed and breakfast. I couldn't go through that again.
I pulled out some lipstick and applied it to try and make me look less ill. My hands were shaking like mad, and I gave up after it wouldn't go on properly. A Pakistani cleaner stood nearby dressed in a deep blue overall. "I'm going to America, to live, for good", I smiled at her.

She looked at me curiously, "English no good", and turned and carried on pushing the mop backwards and forwards slowly across the same piece of floor.

I put the lipstick back in my handbag and noticed as I was doing so, the letter from Ian Brady that Phil had given me.

I could hear my flight being called up over the tannoy, the gate number to proceed to and the last call. I must have missed it before.

I zipped up my handbag, went to pick up my case then turned round and just made it into one of the toilets before I threw up. I couldn't go, I couldn't do it. I stared at myself for a whole minute, then with the taste of vomit still in my mouth and my stomach still churning round I picked up my case and ran through the departure lounge, through all the people hugging their goodbyes at the gate, weighed in my case and got directed towards the gate where the plane was leaving from.

I'd forgotten the letter tucked safely away in my handbag, and I forgot about everything I was leaving behind as the plane careered around and moved off along the runway.

PART TWO

New York

N.B. THE NEWSPAPER ARTICLES REFERRED TO IN THIS CHAPTER
ARE REPRODUCED WITH THE KIND PERMISSION OF THE EDITOR
OF THE SUNDAY PEOPLE. LETTERS FROM IAN BRADY HAVE ALSO
BEEN REPRODUCED AND ARE USED TO END THIS PERIOD OF
CHRISTINE'S LIFE . . . SHE HAS NEVER BEEN TO SEE IAN BRADY
SINCE THE TIME SHE WAS TAKEN TO PARK LANE BY THE
REPORTERS, PHIL HALL AND TED HYNDS.

Dear Christine,

Many thanks for your latest letter and the photocopies of pages from a book you're reading. // I've just eaten a half pound box of coffee cream chocolates and am smoking a Gauloises Caporal. This has put me in a mood to write. // How come you never acknowledge receipt of my letters when you write? // You are like a yo-yo in regard to New York. One minute you're going, the next staying. A love-hate relationship. // So you've broken with The People. Is it actually sold in New York? I wondered how you always knew what they were printing. You certainly seem to regard the reporters you knew there with some affection. // I'll be seeing Lord L this week. I've no official fish frying at present, so I expect the visit will be social and relaxed. // A new thing has started here — a patient can have his photo taken with a visitor. The official hospital photographer does it for £1. A Polaroid photo. Naturally I don't like being photographed. // You seem to spend a lot of time reading about esoteric subjects, the latest being clairvoyance. I use the Tarot but not at a mystical level, purely psychological (I took two courses in psychology — the Aldermaston College and the British Institute of Practical Psychology). You must learn that people waste most of their lives trying to be what they are not. Life isn't a rehearsal, you only get one performance. All physical solutions to man's ills are as transitory as Man himself. A subject I've studied most deeply is auto-hypnosis. Always seek the peak experience. Exercise the will, don't let it become flabby and robotic. It requires self-awareness and conscious control/consciousness. Depression can be dispelled by a simple device — simply concentrate totally on any object for five or so minutes and you will see reality as a whole, as though through a wide-angle lens. There are two planes of consciousness; one is linear, static and mundane. Intense consciousness & freedom is vertical, it stabs like a dagger and awakens the mind. The Roman emperor Marcus Aurelius said: "Live as though you were on the point of death, as if every moment were an unexpected gift." // It's a pity that knowledge is usually only acquired at the expense of years. How often have you heard people say, "If only I could be young again with the knowledge I have now!"? Energy is dissipated in youth — Viele Hunde sind der Tod der Hasen. I broke through the constraints of morality and legality but forgot to build boundaries strong enough to contain myself. Therefore, like an explosion, I allowed all my energies to dissipate in empty space. // Laugh. You probably don't know what I'm talking about — or worse, perhaps I don't! // I wish you would stop the habit of speculating what I might be up to in this and that; the doctor who reads my incoming mail may think I've given you reason to speculate along such lines. The truth re other murders are as follows (the police have all these details) : The man killed on waste-ground in Manchester. The police questioned M and I months later when we were under arrest, but we gave them nothing. So they "cleared the books" by charging a mentally retarded man. And now they're embarrassed by the facts. Similarly, the woman thrown into the canal. Questions but no answers. So they cleared the books and called it suicide though there was no note. The man stabbed in a Glasgow street — the police are maintaining they don't keep records that old. A lie, so I presume they're hiding something. The man shot at Loch Long. The Scottish police (in 65/66) searched along the wrong loch, Loch Lomond, which is separated from Loch Long by four miles of land. The man shot in the moor — a favour to a friend, who in turn did me a favour by owing the river Ousse to rid me of a danger. The police are extremely interested in this, but I refuse to co-operate as there is a "thread" that could lead to the friend. // Why do you mention Rannoch Moor? I know it. It is just behind Glencoe and the Three Sisters (mountains). // I liked your poem. My favourite poets are Wm Blake and Wm Wordsworth. Read any ..

* so that you can't bite the tube.

...my hunger strikes in prison? The first 28 days; second, 58; third, 72; and the rest of the 5 months. In all of 2 strikes I also refused to drink any water and I was being force-fed by —

— Being fed* with [tied] legs, arms and a..., put a wooden block into your throat so they pass the tube through a — they pass the tube through a tube on the flats, down the throat and to the stomach, and they hand the [food] (milk, glucose, etc.) down a funnel to the upper end of the tube and into the tube.

* so that you can't bite the tube.

...discomfort you gave of your life with discomfort... It's very moving. You forced harvest to... to say the least, unlucky, to be... very long them. Are they still alive? Yo you used to hang around the skulls — I was there. Actually, those in end collapse, the top landings used in the...

scrubland itself. Did you ever converse with any of them?

I know that you're really opened up to me in your letters, leaving yourself vulnerable. So I want to assure you that after I reply to letters (all letters, not only yours) I destroy them to make sure that, if I drop dead, no social letters will fall into the hands of the media. And that's why I request everybody (that I write to) to destroy all of my letters in return.

M? She forgot the Parable of the Mustard.

Nietzsche? Yep, I've read him. His two most important works are "Der Wille zur Macht" and "Also sprach Zarathustra" (my personal copy of this is heavily marked in the margins).

Do you know the music popularly known as "2001," which is played on T.V. almost every time a rocket is shown leaving the launch pad? Well, it's actually part of a piece of music (a "tone poem") composed by Strauss and

29/3/'88

Dear Christine,

Many thanks for your letters, and the card I received telling me you're back in England. What's been going on?

Keep away from the media. That "no surprise visits here, remember, or, you'll be wasting a journey. I don't want anything catching the boat at present. I've got enough problems as it is.

I was going to ask you to contact someone in New York, but now you're back here I'll have to leave the matter for the moment. Are you staying here long?

Re "Michael" — Yes, as you ask, not discuss it in letters to you.

I see you quote Wm Blake to me. Didn't I tell you he's my favourite poet. I have his complete works (over a thousand pages), including his "prophetic" books. Yes, starvation feeds the mind. How long

dicated to Nietzsche, and its entitled "go-spuch Zarathustra." (I have the album). on a quote of Milton's, it's "Better to reign in Hell than serve in Heaven." This is spoken by Lucifer in "Paradise Lost".

Basically I'm a really good writer, you know. Stream of consciousness style you have across as totally spontaneous. When very relaxed I sometimes indulge in this sort of thing. But most of the time from a ward.

Well, it's almost dinner-time, and I to put this letter in the post, in case you change address again.

til next time —

Ta ta. Love n

Jan xx

MYRA HINDLEY AND IAN BRADY

THE MOORS
MURDERERS

NEW YORK

I think 'they' were the first thing I remember about America. I'd been there about an hour or so when I first set eyes on them.

The coach from the airport had taken me into Manhattan and I'd looked around me and thought to myself 'No this isn't it, this isn't where I wanted to go'. And I'd flagged down one of those yellow cabs and asked him to take me to the centre. The very centre.

I remember that day very clearly when I think back. It was about five o'clock in the evening and my suitcase, with all my worldly possessions sat inside, locked in the taxi driver's boot, and I sat in the back seat, looking out the window and wondering where the hell I was going.

I was in the cab about ten minutes or so when the scenery started to change and we turned into Broadway and for the first time I looked ahead of me and gasped.

The Radio in the taxi was playing that Michael Jackson song that was popular at the time, "Bad" I think it was, and the car jogged around as he weaved in and out of the traffic while horns honked and I watched the way everyone in the road seemed to be in some sort of hurry.

As we got nearer to the centre of Broadway the buildings seemed to get bigger and the people I could see out of the window walking along the street looked stranger.

Some of them were dressed as cowboys or in gold lurex tops, way out things and there were black people playing cards in the street and gathered around burning brassieres like they did in the Rocky films.

The taxi driver screeched to a halt, jumped out and heaved my suitcase onto the pavement collected his fare and sped off. And it was Times Square he'd dropped me at, and I wandered off into the crowds.

I didn't know in which direction to go, and the other side of the street looked more interesting so I lugged my suitcase along behind me and went to cross the street. I was halfway across the road when a car going the wrong way skidded to a halt, and I turned, terrified, I stood there looking at him until I realised of course they all drove on the different side of the road over here, and I stood there thinking about that and he honked the horn loudly and leant out of his window and shouted at me. "This is New York baby, wakey wakey." I ran across the rest of the way and stood the suitcase at my feet staring at all the surroundings.

It was mid-October but I'd packed my coat in my suitcase in case it was too bulky on the plane so I stood there shivering in a T-shirt and jeans.

I was standing there staring up at the buildings, the sun had come out and it made everything seem stranger than it did already; lit up by the golden glow. Everywhere seemed crowded and people kept pushing into me, so it was sort of like Oxford Street at Christmas but it looked like it was summer.

I walked along then, along Broadway it was, and they'd caught my eye nearly straight away. I remember thinking that it was some sort of street entertainment and I'd hurried over and moved excitedly to the front of the crowd and stood there with my suitcase at my feet.

They were speaking through a microphone or one of them was, and I noticed that they were all black. And they were dressed in red and gold robes, with huge white turbans on their heads but then there were some of them dressed in military gear so they looked like soldiers guarding the others.

They were all different ages but mostly older mostly about forty-five or so, or the one holding the microphone certainly was. He had dark glasses and was addressing a young black girl who'd been in the crowds I saw gathered around them. I remember as I joined them, a whole group of them standing behind the speaker laughing and looking in my direction. I looked behind me then down at myself nervously wondering what it was that they were laughing at.

The speaker caught their laughter and turned his gaze to me, "Well, you're not American are you?" he shouted down the microphone in that unique black-American accent.

I stood there wondering how he knew that, when he called me over to him. "Now, I want you to tell everybody who you think Jesus looks like."

I laughed and smiled at him, thinking it was some sort of routine he was doing or a trick question "Er. Robert Powell, I suppose," I said back grinning. He didn't know who Robert Powell was and looked at me strangely and then carried on talking. I stood back near my suitcase and stared up at the buildings around me, and listened, mesmerised by the sound of the police siren and the distinctive wail that I'd only heard on films before.

I turned my attention back to the speaker in front of me, he had finished his act, and he was making way for another man who stood behind him.

I made to go then, I remember I didn't like the look of him. He was about seven foot tall and big and about forty or so like the other one, but he looked kind of angry. He had a thick black beard, strong teeth and dark marmalade colour eyes and a nose that seemed crinkled up into a perpetual snarl so his whole face or whole person looked like it belonged in wartime or on a battlefield, not in peace-time, and not dressed like a king or priest that he was claiming to be.

I watched him as he ran his dark eyes over the audience and fixed the microphone in front of him to the right angle.

And then he started to talk. And I don't know what it was but it was like the feeling you get when you read a book that takes you totally out of yourself. He seemed to have some sort of energy that came pouring out of him via his speech, a sort of inspired way and it left me almost breathless and hypnotised by its force and power.

He seemed to have clicked into something and was letting it pour through him. So the effect was almost beautiful and the look in his eyes, as he looked out on the listening crowd like something from another world.

I stared up at him absorbed, and didn't notice that around me darkness had fallen on Times Square and neon lights from the great billboards threw out an unearthly light over the pale faces dripping in jewellery off to see the latest show or play along Broadway.

"Look at them," he shouted down the microphone, "they are so wrapped up in their shows and themselves and their pleasures they do not realise that this isn't real, this is Disneyland. God is the only reality. Look to spirit for your fulfilment and for your saviour, these people are all lost, dependent on something that is a flimsy illusion, here one minute, gone the next. Not like God. Not like the spiritual, both are one and the same and they are solid and eternal, and will never let you down."

I stood and listened and looked around at the tall buildings as he spoke. So this was what America was like, full of people who loved God, and thought it was all unreal, just like me. My people. And I stood there and felt as if somehow, I belonged. I really belonged there, and I had my suitcase at my feet 300 dollars in it, it was all I had, but I didn't care, I'd found somewhere that was going to be my home, at last and after all the looking.

He was still talking, a kind of rage of anger against the normal values and way of life and devotion to materialism and absence of God.

He held up the huge Bible in front of him and read from it.

"Love not the world or the things that are in the world. If any man love the world the love of the father is not in him. For all that is in the world the lust of the flesh and the lust of the eyes and the pride of life is not of the Father but is of the world."

And I listened to what he said from the Bible and I thought, 'that's funny I've never heard that before' I'd always thought that people who loved life and the world automatically loved God. I hated the world and I hated living and I thought that made me evil.

I felt a warm glow inside towards him, he was teaching me, and he felt so much like the way I did, and I was looking at him, and I looked up and he was staring straight at me.

He beckoned me over to him, then held out his hand and I walked towards him.

"Hold out your hand, now hold it up against mine and tell me the difference."

I stood there speechless, not understanding what he meant or what he wanted me to say.

"Tell me the difference," he said again and I looked up at him and tried to smile, "I can't see a difference."

181

And I put my hand down, and stepped back, not taking my eyes off him, and not expecting what he said next. "The difference is I am black and you are white. You are the child of Satan, the seed of Esau."

I stared back at him, then looked wildly round behind me, and then gasped quietly. I was surrounded by a huge crowd of nearly sixty or so black men, all half mesmerised by the speaker and looking at me angrily. And I turned back to him, and he was speaking again, and it was even more impassioned than before. The white man was responsible for the fall of man, the white man was the maker of the empty Godless world we lived in.

I looked at the ground, my knees almost buckled in front of me. I shone out stupidly amongst the crowd of black men, small white face with pale hair, right in the front of the crowd. And I hadn't even realised. I couldn't move then, everyone would have watched me moving away, and I was right under his stare. I was too scared to move so I just stood there, and pictured myself beaten and bloodied and walking around that place with my suitcase taken and all my money gone. And he was still talking on and on down the microphone, "I have never met a white person that I have liked, every one of them full of greed and hatred, not one, not even one."

I felt a pain inside that was a sharp contrast to the warmth I'd felt earlier and all of a sudden I was alone again. A stranger amongst strangers who didn't belong.

His speech was gathering more and more momentum with every sentence; His face beaded in sweat; teeth bared until his face resembled that of an animal, a wolf or a lion, as he screamed out "Jesus was a Racist. I am a Racist."

He hung up the microphone then turned and stood and clung to the railings along the side of the road; the great big frame of him shaking in anger and trembling with energy spent.

The others gathered round him and put their hands on his shoulders to try and comfort him. And then with his back to me and another speaker moving forward, I somehow felt an inner urge to go.

I moved off and mingled amongst the crowds of Times Square, the thought of him and the picture of his face still strong in my mind.

I found a small bed and breakfast hotel off 50th Street and although I booked in there for a few nights I made up my mind that the next day I'd look for a proper room to rent and a job.

I laid in bed that night and felt a bit lost. I wondered what would happen if I didn't find a job or get somewhere to live then I pushed the idea out of my mind. I looked at the clock it was nearly ten o'clock. I'd been told by a woman on the plane not to go out after eight o'clock in the city, and I sat there thinking, about what I was doing. Here I was in New York City for the first time and I was in bed at ten o'clock. And I said to myself "Come on stupid, get up and go out." And I pulled my boots on, brushed my hair and put on some more make-up and took in the glassy eyed look that stared back at me from the mirror.

I stuffed my money under the pillow in the hotel room, apart from ten dollars that I took with me, and hid my handbag behind the shower and walked out of the hotel and along to Broadway. I headed in the direction of 47th Street and I told myself I was just coincidentally going in that direction and it wasn't that I wanted to see if 'they' were still there.

Times Square was as vibrant and active as some sort of giant party. Black men came out of darkened doorways whispering "smoke smoke" and music seemed to be coming from just about everywhere. Good time girls paraded up and down the street in short brightly coloured mini skirts with wild hairstyles and approached the long limousines that cruised slowly past.

Music and noise came from every doorway and I went into a nearby bar and ordered a beer, and when he served it up without a glass, I swigged it straight from the bottle like everyone else appeared to be doing. The juke box blared out a Dire Straits number and I finished off the beer and went out back into the noise of the street.

The party atmosphere was still continuing and a man stood up through the sun roof of a passing car and blasted out a tune on a trumpet he was holding, and heads turned and smiled and stared. But not me, I felt unreal and empty and stood there leaning against a shop window front, and I felt that somehow, something was incredibly wrong

The beer had done nothing for me, and I bought a hot dog covered in mustard and walked along again chewing that.

Nightclub bouncers blocked the doors from various nightclubs along the way, I picked one of them and paid the entrance fee and sat down at the bar inside it.

It was fairly dark inside and as soon as I sat down a middle aged man with fair hair came and sat next to me.

His name was Ed and he was in New York on business and staying at the hotel around the corner. I sat and exchanged small talk with him when the music allowed it and drunk Bacardi and Coke continuously. The night wore on and I looked around the Club, it was full of fairly youngish people and Ed looked a bit out of place "D'you like these kind of places then?" I asked him and watched his reaction. He told me that he did, and I took another swig of my drink and looked up at the huge cinema screen they had hanging over the dance floor; a video was playing in time to the music and it showed a couple making love; writhing about near naked, bodies glistening with sweat as they became carried away in each others sex.

184

Ed saw me watching it intensely and grinned at me suggestively "It's good isn't it, very erotic." I leant forward over the bar and put my head in my hands and let the tears flow down my face.

It took him a long time to realise my unhappiness, but when he did, he blamed himself and apologised for any insinuations he'd made.

"No, no it's alright," I said it's not you, It's me, I mean I've only come here today and I thought, I don't know what I thought but I know I haven't come here for this. I feel funny. Ever since, well I'm not sure, but I feel funny like nothings real, and if it is real it's like those two up there, like wrong y'know; somehow wrong, not right, not good. Do you know what I mean?" I swigged back more drink, and it made the feeling worse and I cried some more.

I was still crying when I looked up and noticed he'd gone. Then I left the club and made my way home to the hotel room. I went straight to bed without taking off my make-up and lay there in the darkness. It was strange. It was like I heard the man's voice, the man that I'd just left, Ed, like I heard it really clear like in my head say "Crazy broad, I don't know what she was laying on me crying like that," and I turned over and closed my eyes and I was just drifting off to sleep when I heard a loud conversation going on, which seemed to be coming from the room above. Two men's voices in conspiratorial whispers and I remember smiling to myself, closing my eyes and falling off to sleep again.

And then I remembered it next morning, and assumed it was the amount of drink I'd consumed or maybe someone just talking in the room above me. But it was funny because it sounded as if it was two men actually in the room with me and I could hear them. I just couldn't see them.

The first step the next day was to find a room so I bought a local newspaper and stood in the foyer of the small hotel to phone round the different advertisements for rooms to let.

185

I'd phoned quite a few and received the same answer over and over; either "the room's gone" or "if you haven't got a job you can't stay here." It was the second to last one I'd phoned when someone who introduced themselves as Joe answered the phone. I warmed to him straight away. He seemed kind and friendly and asked whether I was cold, and said in a pure New York accent "Get your butt over here now, and rent my room, I like the sound of your voice."

Over here turned out to be Staten Island, and I had to get the number one train all the way downtown to the end of the line, South Ferry. I had to board the huge Staten Island Ferry which took everybody backwards and forwards from Manhattan Island. That day was the first time on the dusty old ferry and it took my breath away. I stood out on deck, and marvelled at the huge Statue of Liberty as the boat went speeding past it.

Joe looked like the late comedian Roy Kinnear: Huge and fat and full of fun.

He took me in his small white beaten up old van to view the various rooms he had in different houses he owned throughout the island.

He had three houses in all and I saw them each in turn and got more depressed by the minute. Small, depressing dark dank rooms in old run down houses. He noticed my depression and slapped my knee, "What's up with you, you look like you're going to cry? Do you want some of this, this'll cheer you up." He pulled out a polythene bag of ground up grass.

"No thanks", I laughed, "I hate that stuff. Even the smell of it makes me ill."

He shoved it back in his pocket and started the car again and drove the car back up towards the ferry terminal and took the car along to Richmond Terrace near Port St George the road that ran along the water's edge, and pulled up in front of a huge white painted house that stood deserted on its own on a kind of hill. It reminded me of the house they used in the film Psycho. And I wondered why

186

Joe had stopped the car, until he told me that it was his, and it was the last one he had to show me.

The house, 1836 Richmond Terrace, was fronted by a huge burnt out garden and ringed with a barbed wire fence and a huge gate.
Joe explained that before he'd bought it, it had been a half way house for senile old men from the mental home in Port St George and the locals hadn't liked the idea of the old men living there so they'd tried to burn it down.

The garden and the bottom of the house were black from the fire and it made the lonely old house look sad somehow. Even the small bushes in the garden were broken off and stood with only their stalks, visible, while the leaves had been destroyed by the fire.

Joe unlocked the front door and we wiped our feet on the dusty old mat that stood on the huge wooden veranda at the front of the house. I pushed at a huge settee that was on some sort of frame and it swung backwards and forwards making huge creaking noises as dust came flying off its covers.

Joe led the way and I followed him up a huge flight of stairs, on and on until we'd gone up three flights. I thought we'd come to the top of the house but he opened an old battered white painted door and another flight of stairs appeared, so I followed him up those until we came to a small dark attic room, way way up at the top of the house.

I took in the huge double bed in the centre of the room, the windows that looked out onto the various boats coming into the island, and the dark wooden crucifix pinned on the wall. It looked like a room a nun would have in a convent, spartan and quiet, and it seemed like it was so remote that it was cut off from the rest of the world.

Joe had told me that he'd rented it to a girl before me, and driving past one

187

night he'd heard her screams and laughs and went up outside the door to hear her chanting and talking, even though he knew she was alone, and she'd just disappeared one day and left all her stuff there, and he'd had to put it in storage; but she'd never returned for it. The story of my predecessor did nothing to lighten my nerves about the place. It was so cut off, even the house itself deserted almost, far from the others, set back on a slope it stood with its sadness and its secrets.

I paid Joe a small amount of money for the small attic room and unpacked my case and hung up my clothes in the small closet. The only others in the house were three old men who stayed in the lower rooms.

One old man of seventy who Joe called 'Frankie' because the man thought he was Frank Sinatra, had come from the mental home in Port St George. He'd spent all his life in the home as his parents had put him there as a child, and he was Joe's favourite; he'd try to come over regularly to chat to him and would never have anything bad to say about old Frankie.

Then on the bottom floor next to the downstairs toilet there was a small Mexican of about sixty five. I'd borrow cigarettes off him, knocking on his door at all hours, but he always answered it with a smile while clutching two or three stale Marlboros.

On the middle floor lived an old Jamaican called Joe, who was forever ironing his clothes. He'd have to put the ironing board up in the hallway as his room was so small.

He was the only one there who worked; and he worked nights. I'd often watch him leave from out of my window; his old bent body making his way down the road through the snow at three o'clock in the morning.

I wondered about him. Would he die there? there in that little room with nothing; Would he one day fall over in the snow in the cold night on the way to work, with no-one finding him or noticing him missing until he died. His possessions nothing but the clothes he stood up in.

Could someone really go through their lives and end up old, alone and poor and friendless in a small little room? I looked at myself on some lonely nights and knew how easy it could be. Once alone, always alone.

I'd been doing various jobs around then, like waitressing, and washing up, but not lasting long in them because they'd soon find out I was working illegally when I couldn't produce a social security card. So I did temporary work most of the time.

I'd enjoy the Staten Island Ferry ride. I'd get to and from Manhattan where I mostly worked. It was only a dollar fare, and most of the people on the Island commuted on a daily basis. I couldn't make up my mind which I liked best; the view of Manhattan in the early mornings from the upper deck of the ferry, wind blowing my hair around and the sun all glowy just coming up from behind the concrete skyscrapers of Manhattan, or the nighttimes when I went back to Staten Island and looked back on the city lit-up like the sequins on a beautiful dress or a handful of diamonds.

It was strange though: I'd look at the views and that famous skyline and I should've felt excited. Here I was in New York; a new start, a new life, I should've felt excited and happy and yet I felt somehow flat and empty, and nothing was touching me. Like it is in a dream, it was like some sort of dream going on around me, and nothing at all seemed real. It was just some great big illusion that somehow everyone was wrapped up in, and all except for me, I was the only one that had woken up and I felt like someone who has woken up one day to find that there is no-one else left in the world but him, and he goes running around the streets and panicking and looking for any signs of life, but realises with a growing sense of horror that he is alone.

I thought back around that time to the psychic I'd seen, and how all his predictions had somehow strangely seemed to have happened to me in quick succession and I thought about his story about J. Someone with the initial J who was me. And I'd smiled to myself. Ever since everything else had come true I'd been dead nervous about meeting someone awful with the name beginning with J. I didn't want to get married and I couldn't imagine meeting someone who was me, the idea of a fair haired blue eyed man repulsed me. I normally preferred dark haired men, and I'd been panicking all around my brother's birthday when he said I'd meet him, but the day had passed Oct 4th, the day I'd landed in New York and I'd met no-one of that name and I felt kind of relieved really. At least the psychic had been wrong about something.

I was working round then at a place called Cafe 43 on 43rd and Broadway. It was early November, and it was snowing great heavy thick flakes and I'd tramped along in it like a kid the first time I'd seen it. Times Square looked beautiful in the snow like a picture postcard but I wasn't used to the extremes of cold temperature and I had a kind of almost perpetual cold from the bitter icy winds that could chill right down to your bone.

I kept having time off when I should have been working and I'd got behind with the rent and I was barely eating, just maybe a bagel in the morning then another one at nights. Phil Hall phoned me around then, he said it was to check to see if I was ok, but I knew it was to see if I'd replied to Ian, saying he may be my father. I'd given him the phone number of the payphone we had in the hallway, then wished I hadn't when he kept phoning.

It was during one of the conversations that I told him about the Children of Israel the Black Racist group I'd heard speaking.

"That would make an excellent story, well it would if they had links in this country or intended coming here," Phil enthused.

I'd hesitated then thought of the huge speaker in the red robes talking on the street corner and felt a sudden urge to help him somehow or do something for him.

"Phil, I think they did mention something like that in their speech," I said, then held my breath waiting for his reaction.

"Well, I'll check up on it with our contacts in New York and then if you're right we'll do a story on them."

I put down the phone then rushed back upstairs to see if I'd still got the leaflet I'd picked up after I'd heard them speak. It was at the bottom of my handbag, and there it was The Children of Israel, 125th and Amsterdam, Harlem and a phone number. I went to go downstairs to phone the number, but then thought again; it said on the leaflet that they always spoke at around the same time on Saturdays and Sundays and tomorrow was a Saturday.

It was cold when I stood there waiting on the corner of 47th Street. I was trembling inside but I wondered was it all the cold or some of it the fear of talking to him, someone that seemed to have that much force, that much power. I must have been early, or they must have been late, because I was standing there for about an hour when I thought they weren't coming so I decided to phone.

It was an old man who answered the phone, and I'd asked him had I got the right day for the Children of Israel on 47th Street as they weren't there yet. "Oh and I wanted to see the speaker the one in the red robe."

"That's Lahab," he told me, "and they are coming, they're leaving now."

By seven thirty they still hadn't turned up so I went and sat in a coffee bar, and told myself to relax and stop feeling so nervous, as my hands were shaking.

191

And I kept wondering what I'd say to him, the angry strong looking man I'd seen speaking when I'd first come to New York a month earlier. I mean what would he be like; would he talk to me or just stand in silence and regard me in hatred because of his Racism?

And then how would I explain to him about the story, when I was so terrified of him? I came out of the coffee bar and headed for 47th and Broadway and I just got a few yards away when I realised that he was there.

I stopped dead in my tracks with fright and stared at him; everything I had planned to say in my mind suddenly left me, and I just stood there stupidly staring.

He was dressed in black this time, all black, a black suede jacket with a fringe on the sleeves and on the pockets and black trousers with long black boots over the tops of them. He looked like a trapper or something like that, or he would've done if it hadn't been for the white turban bound round his head.

He was standing talking to one of the other black men 'the brothers' the old man on the phone had called them, about which piece in the Bible to quote. And it looked funny really, two men pouring over the Bible amongst all that decadence of the theatre district, and Broadway, and the nearby sex shops on 42nd Street. I heard the other black man say to him "There's your friend." And he looked up and I braced myself.

The cold weather had made his face look fresh and ruddy and his eyes shiny with the wind and he looked at me, in the protective way an adult might look at a child, but with an added friendliness and interest.

He moved towards me, and looked back towards a black kind of jeep type thing. "Just wait while I park my car and I'll come back and I'll find somewhere for us to sit and talk." And he went off and I stood there leant up against the front of the restaurant, and I felt almost dizzy.

He came back in a few minutes and I followed him along Broadway trying to look at him a bit more closely.

It was nearly eight o'clock by then and the theatre goers were all out and about; dressed up couples decked out in fur and jewellery and it was dark already and starting to turn into that party type atmosphere that it had after dark in Times Square. I was wondering did we look a strange couple when he turned into the doorway of one of those fast food places ordered himself some fried chicken and I followed him to a table and sat beside him and drank the Coke I'd ordered.

He was already swallowing down chicken with the aid of his hands, fingers covered in grease and lips shiny and wet.

I noticed that he ate like a man starved, and with a total concentration as if the only thing that existed at that particular moment was the fried chicken. He looked like an animal again, but this time a lion pulling apart its prey after a kill.

I was staring at him, and he looked up at me, "So what is it that you want to talk to me about?" He had a voice that was the strongest and deepest I'd ever heard, and he carried on eating as if it didn't really matter whether I told him or not.

I pulled out the story I'd roughly drafted to Phil, and showed a copy to Lahab. I'd called it 'Black Racists Come To Britain'. I stared at him intensely while he looked at it, "You write well, you're a journalist then" he said slowly.

I hesitated, then thought he'd probably wonder why I had written it so I told him that I was a reporter. He'd think that I was mad if I'd told him, that I thought he should be broadcasting his message from somewhere where everyone would hear, not just those gathered on 47th Street. Talking with all the power and the force that he had, explaining that it was all unreal, it was all Disneyland and the only thing that mattered was God and Spirit. I thought of last time I'd heard him speak and how, when he'd quoted from the Bible about people who didn't love the world having God in them. And I'd thought maybe God was different to the judgmental God I'd been taught about in childhood, and said Goodbye to in the Catholic Church just before I'd visited Ian. Maybe God wasn't like that; maybe he was the God that this man talked about; the God of the other world, the God that was spirit.

And I'd bought a Bible after that and read it for the first time and I'd read different things in it that all spoke of this spirit that he'd preached about.

I was thinking about this when I realised that I hadn't answered his question and he was watching me, a look of interest on his face.

"Yes, I am a journalist, I'm sort of freelance though," I fibbed, and watched his face intently to see if he could detect my lies. "The only thing is my office will probably be in contact with you to see if you do have offices and contacts in London, so you'd best say you do."

He grinned up at me, as he realised what I was saying. "We could be starting a revolution here you know."

I phoned Phil Hall the next day; the story was definitely in. "Read it to me then, what you've written," I said excitedly.
The story he read back to me was exactly as I'd written and yet he paused and asked me did I like it, and I thought to myself, well o.k. if he wants the credit, I don't care. And then he paused for breath, "Oh and here's something you didn't manage to find out," he began smugly, "I spoke to a reporter in New York, who told me all about them. They send out little boys to collect money for them for a so called charity, that is really for themselves. Also, they

194

sexually abuse them, and they have earned some of the money to support themselves with child pornography. I was stunned silent on the end of the phone, "No, that's not true, I know it's not true."

"You've known them for five minutes," said Phil mockingly, "this reporter I spoke to told me all about them."

I slammed down the phone on him, and ran back upstairs and looked at myself in the mirror as I picked up a hairbrush and brushed my hair with long hard strokes, What was the matter with me? Was it something within me that was evil, that felt deeply attracted to evil?

I phoned the number of the Children of Israel and left my phone number for Lahab, to ring me back.

The next day he telephoned me and we arranged to meet outside Rockefeller Center at two o'clock in the afternoon.

We went into an empty Japanese restaurant and sat up at the bar. I sipped a Perrier and watched him as he delved into plateloads of noodles and chicken wings, which he again ate, with his fingers. seemingly half hypnotised as he ravished the food in front of him.
I relayed the story of what had appeared in the People, then leant back and watched him waiting for some kind of reaction.

"And how do you know that I am not a molester of small children?" he asked quietly. "Well I know someone else who they say is that sort of person and although he did do those things, I know, I believe," I paused, "that in some way and somehow he didn't do it at all," I looked at him, "do you know what I mean?"

"Yes, I do know what you mean, things can happen in the physical and be not

195

at all like they appear to be. That is because the physical is mostly illusion and lies."

"Are you very spiritual?" I asked him, and waited for him to answer.
He paused as he was eating, and looked at me "As spiritual as you are," he answered.
"Oh I'm not spiritual, I'm not even religious, I haven't been to mass in ages."
"You rely, or seem to rely on what your inner self tells you, and not on your reason, and that is spiritual."

I stared at him and took a sip from the Perrier water in front of me. I was watching him, and thinking in my mind whether or not to tell him about how I'd been feeling lately, how everything was seeming sort of unreal and people appeared alien to me.

"Are you alone in New York?" he asked.
"Yes, well I'm alone anyway. I was brought up in an orphanage."
"And why are you here, what is it that you're running from?"
"Oh I'm not running from anything I'm looking, looking for something."
"Well, the way you look, it won't be long before someone snaps you up, a rich man to look after you."
"Oh I don't want that, not money," I said and looked at him, hurt by his comment.

I turned and stared out the window. It was a grey afternoon and it had started to drizzle. A large black tramp walked past the window with a sign round his neck 'I am homeless, please help me'. And he leant down and scavenged in the street dustbin and pulled out the remnants of an ice-lolly and began to eat it. He looked old and incredibly tired and he stooped as he walked on feet bound up with some sort of rags. And then, while I was still staring out the window, a girl went past; tight low cut top, a gold lamé mini skirt and long dark flowing hair. She tossed her hair about as she walked, revelling in her sensuality; and her attractiveness drew stares from everyone passing by. Cars went past splashing up water from the puddles in the kerbs, long long limousines filled with fur coated people off to find some fun.

"Well, then are you looking for where you belong, looking for your home" he said as he woke me from my thoughts. His gaze followed mine out the window, "I know what it is you're looking for. You're looking for God. You're looking for God in New York City," and he started to laugh, but it sounded hollow and empty.

We sat in silence for a while which I didn't notice, I was too deep in my own thoughts, when he stood up to leave.

"I'll phone The Sunday People to make sure they take that bit out, about the molesting of kids and stick to the original story that I wrote" I told him as he took out some dollar bills and paid the waitress for his dinner.

We walked to the corner of the street together then turned and went our separate ways; I'd only walked a few feet when I turned to stare after him as he walked off in the opposite direction. That old feeling of loneliness swept over me.

I felt a deep regret for not confiding in him, for not telling him how I felt, yet it would've been pathetic; he was a stranger, I didn't know him. And yet who else could I tell? I was becoming frightened inside about some sort of change that was going on. It was like a cut-off sort of feeling an increasingly separated feeling from other people, that was more than just a loneliness. It was like a strange feeling of alienation towards everything and everyone.
I'd always felt as if I didn't belong, and the suspicion that I was somehow different, and it was like I was changing, changing more into what I knew myself to be all the time. The thing that had made me different from the others was getting stronger and I didn't understand it.

It was like I was outside watching myself. Detached. And then when I was in

197

myself, it was like a kind of thick glass was forming around me and cutting me off from everything and everyone. And I was looking at them from within this goldfish bowl, looking out on the people and they seemed kind of like puppets and marionettes not like people at all, unreal and their world, and the things in it, was unreal as well.

And this feeling terrified me, I couldn't stand so much aloneness. I couldn't bear it.

I phoned Phil and managed to get through to him on Tuesday. I'd looked in the copy of The People in Hotalings and there had been no article. He was bright and breezy on the other end of the phone, "Oh I scrapped the story in the end, what with you saying they'd sue us if we printed it."

"They'd sue you and I would help them sue you if you printed that child pornography lies; it just isn't true," I said angrily.

"Oh I know it isn't true, I checked deeper into it, and you were right, it's some sort of religious group in Miami with a similar name, someone had got them confused."

"But you would've printed it though if I hadn't stopped you" I said, still irritated.
"It was probably quite lucky that you found out."
"Found out what? I just knew, that's all. Why do you seem to hate them. They are good people."
"Religious nuts. Cranks that's all, Christine . . .. Just a bunch of weirdos, who" . . . .

I hung up on him in mid-sentence, then thought about how I'd kissed him, and even wanted him; how once I had thought him so clever and so wise. Funny how we only see things in people that we want to see, and then felt angry with them later for letting us down; it was really our own fault for not seeing them properly in the first place; and then I wondered that if everyone saw each other as they really were, would any of us ever speak to each other?

I couldn't get hold of Lahab via the phone number of their headquarters, so I turned up at one of their public speakings on 47th Street the following Friday.

He was there and he looked over at me and I couldn't bring myself to tell him; there would be no story.

I told him, although it hadn't appeared this week it would probably be in next week's.

He looked at me with a sort of sadness."You're white, why should you help us anyway?"

He turned away before I could answer and then took his turn behind one of the others to speak through the microphone.

And I wondered how he'd feel when he found out there would be no story. The rest of the group had been annoyed when I'd singled him out for my attention and he'd told them about how the newspaper story focused on him. How would they react, when they discovered there was no story? Would they make him feel a fool, and make me out to be a liar? Would he lose face for believing me in the first place?

His speech again was delivered with a kind of force behind it, almost a hate, All about the stupidity of man, the futility of their existence and the absence of God in their lives. He seemed to have in him a well developed, sincere yearning for God and while he was talking to the crowd, things came out about his life; He was a Vietnam war veteran, and on returning from the war he'd been unable to settle down to the apple pie existence and he'd felt lost, alienated. His experiences and the painful sights he had seen in the war making him aware of the low quality of normal everyday life, and he'd looked for some meaning to it, he'd even become a Muslim for six years, until he realised that that "wasn't it" as he put it. And now at forty-five, just two years previously, he said he'd found the brothers. 'The Children of Israel' after one day hearing them speak on 47th Street and he'd said he'd found it, and he wasn't lost any longer.

That the answer was in the philosophy of 'The Children of Israel', the philosophy of race hatred and black supremacy, undeniably lying with the end of the 'Kingdom of the White-Man'. He'd finished speaking and he stood to the side of the group fixing his clothes and I walked over to him and stood there. "If you did have your way and all the white people were wiped out and you saw that a black man had got hold of me and they had a gun to me, just about to kill me, what would you do?."

He glared at me but I continued ignoring his stare: "You said in your speech how you would pull out your guns and kill the white people when the day came, but you wouldn't kill me, because you like me, you do like me, and you wouldn't watch me die. That isn't you! You're full of love, not hate. It's just too much resentful energy, so you think it's hate but it's not, it's love," He stared at me strangely then and I felt I should shut up, but I didn't. Something was urging me on. I continued. "You haven't found yourself at all, these people aren't what you're about, it's God you're looking for, you're like me, it's not hate, not the race hatred you preach. You're just the same as when you came back from Vietnam. You're lost.! You're lost..."
"Shut up" he shouted at me.

And I looked up shocked; he was staring at me with a look of total anger and rage, and I noticed he was trembling. I was just about to leave when one of the brothers shouted. "Didn't your friend like your speech?" and put on a smarmy high pitched girl's voice, "Oh, you didn't mean me, did you?" he continued to mimic.

I left then. I'd done enough damage and it was best that I went away, and I kept on walking towards the 42nd Street subway. I felt like I had a lump inside me, a lump of a sickening pain.

I stayed away from Times Square after that, I didn't need to go near there. Come Fridays and Saturdays I had to resist the urge to go and stand and listen to them speak. Hearing someone else who felt the way I did, even though he preached racism, eased the fear of the strange feelings that I had.

What the hell was wrong with me anyway? Why couldn't I be like everyone else? Why couldn't I want what I had wanted before now seemed futile and pointless. They were just things in the dream, unreal things and wanting them would be like wanting to be permanently asleep. No, there was something else I wanted, needed, with a deep unrelenting yearning that was almost itself a pain; the pain of someone eternally separated from a lover; Always there, it never left me.

Sometimes it was even hard to drag myself out of bed in the mornings. I'd think what the hell is the point, none of it is real, and I'd try to get up but it was as if some sort of energy supply had been switched off and I'd lay on the bed, and cry, and wonder what would become of me. How would I live if I couldn't get up.

And I'd lay there and pray "Please God, please help me, don't make me feel like this, help me to get up, please help me!" . . . I needed someone. Everyone has someone. It was nearly always a family and I had no-one.

And some days I would be able to get up and I'd thank God and I'd do some temporary job like waitressing or handing out leaflets in the street, but I could only work for short periods, and I began to eat very little; one loaf of bread and some salad cream and I'd make it last a week, kept at the bottom of the closet in the old attic room, so it wouldn't go missing from the fridge.
And when I wasn't working, I'd huddle under the blankets in my room, trying to keep warm, and sleep just to pass the time, and to help the day to end . . .

It was a cold winter that year of 1987 and it was coming up to Christmas, a real white New York kind of Christmas. Come in 1988, start anew - start my life again.

I'd have to sleep in my clothes most of the time because of the cold, and the house had no bath just a leaky old shower that threw out lukewarm water, so I never really felt warm or really clean; just permanently freezing, through to my bones.

I remember it was about three weeks before Christmas and the temperature dropped to a degree I had never known in England. The icy winds blew in straight from the north and the needle on the barometer would drop to way below freezing. I was still only eating a loaf of bread a week with salad cream, and I'd developed some sort of cold that made my head feel woozy and muzzy and I felt feverish and I'd sweat during the night then go ice cold, then sweat again.

I'd go once a week to the local store about a mile away in Port St George. I hated going there it was situated in a notorious red light area, and I always trifled to get there and back before it was dark or take the bus.
One night and still ill, it was near nine o'clock and I needed some milk. I wrapped up and made my way through the snow to the small grocers store.

I'd chatted to the old man serving for a while to ease the loneliness, then clutching a brown bag with the milk and some apples I made to go back. For the first time in ages, I actually felt like something to eat.

Just as I came to the corner of Richmond Terrace and within a hundred yards of the house they appeared as if from nowhere, in a car.
"Get in."

I turned to see where the voice had come from.

"Get in, bitch."

202

Two men drove up alongside me, redneck sorts with check shirts and caps on in a beaten up green saloon car.

My legs buckled underneath me in fear and I stumbled but then gathered my step and began to run.

I nearly made it to the house as they screeched the car around and pulled up in front of me; the car blocking my exit.

The one in the passenger seat got out and slammed a baseball bat on the floor.

"You don't need that to beat me up do you?" I shouted at him hoping my pleadings would lessen his anger.

"Get in the fucking car, English bitch," he screamed at me.

And with vomit coming up in to my throat with fear I turned and ran in the opposite direction.

A man was walking down the street opposite me.

I ran into him, sobbing, "Please help me! Please! I think they're going to kill me!"

He looked at me sternly, "You shouldn't be out at this time of night around here." "I live over there." I pointed.

"What alone?"

"Yes," I answered, not thinking.

"Have you got any valuables?"

"No, no I haven't."

The men in the car had driven off.

He walked me to the gate, and I asked him if there was any point in calling the police.

He said there was no point. They wouldn't come anyway, not to this area.

I thanked him for helping me, and walked through the gate, up the path and into the house. When I got up to my room, I lay on the bed, hardly able to breathe my throat thick, and my head throbbing with the oncoming flu, and my narrow escape.

And I was just laying there and I was drifting into a sleep I was so exhausted. And then I noticed something, something different, and my stomach turned in astonishment, and I suddenly realised what it was. It was normally dead silent up near the house, it was deserted, and cars never really came along the road much, much less right up to the house, and I could hear it. A car engine running. A car engine running outside the house.

I ran to the window. It was them looking up to the house. They both got out of the car and walked up to the door and began to kick it and kick it. And I ran to my bedroom door and locked it and sat on the floor in the corner behind the bed, crying silently and whimpering.

The kicking went on and on, and I was imagining what they'd do to me when they got hold of me, and I was praying, 'please don't let them get hold of me' and then I heard shouting like it was the police. The police had seen them and were shouting over to them. Then I heard the car engine again but this time as it roared off.

I unlocked my room door and ran downstairs and opened the front door or what was left of it. I'd have to tell the police what happened, give them a statement.

I flung back the door and instead of the police who I'd been expecting it was him. The one that had helped me before. He told me he'd thought they would come back and he'd walked back to check on me.

I was standing there leaning on the door frame and listening to him, when all of a sudden everything went black and I fell forward and I think he caught me because next thing he was half carrying me up the stairs and I was telling him that I lived right at the very top. My legs would barely take my weight and I was sobbing and shaking uncontrollably.

I lay on the bed and started to go in and out of consciousness and I was aware of him still in my room but walking around it. He hadn't switched the light on and the only light came from the moon outside, and I could only see him very faintly. I kept struggling to keep my eyes open, until he spoke.

"So you've no jewellery or money?"

I opened my eyes again slowly, realising.

He came round and stood in front of me, then leant over and started to tug at the waistband of my trousers. I summoned up all my energy and tried to get up and with that he leant his full weight on top of me, his whole body pushing into mine as he tugged at my trousers and pushed his mouth against mine, tearing against my skin with his unshaven face.

I smelt the smell of stale tobacco and alcohol, something like stale whisky and I gagged and moved my head away.

I thought I was going to pass out again. I summoned every ounce of my remaining strength and with a surge of will pulled myself up.

There was no point in trying to fight him off, I was too weak. I decided to bluff.

"Oh I would. I'd love to, I would, I mean you saved me. And I need a man around. But there's all this pus and stuff, I'm not sure what it is, but it's only a dose. I'll get it cleaned up, then we can or if you don't mind we'll do it now, I don't mind."

He moved away and got off of me, then stood and stared at me in disgust, breathing hard from his aroused state. Then he raised his arm and brought his hand down smack across my face, "Dirty filthy whore."

I felt numb from the blow, then watched in terror as he began smashing anything he could around my room. I didn't have much that was mine but he smashed the big mirror on the wall and went through the drawers and the wardrobe.

Eventually he moved towards the door.

"You've got nothing."

In an afterthought he saw my handbag lying on the floor and went for the purse. There was ten dollars and he took that and left.
I slept all night in the position I was in when he left, then woke next morning to the cruel grey winter light shining in through the windows. I attempted to clear up the room and pick up the fragments of the broken mirror he'd torn off the wall.

As I leant down to pick up a large piece it cut deeply into my hand and blood immediately came pumping to the surface and dripped down onto the darker red of the linoleum.

I couldn't stay there.

I had wages to pick up from Cafe 43, seventy dollars. I found two dollars for the fare and packed my suitcase, tidied myself, showered in bitterly cold water and bound my hand with a cotton headscarf I had, and left. I thought, then, it was forever.

My make-up looked bright and garish as I looked in the hall mirror as I left. I couldn't apply it properly as my right hand was the injured one.

I stood at the bus stop. The snow was deep and it was starting to sleet heavily. Then rain eventually started pelting down, and with no umbrella and still feeling ill with the flu, I was terrified that I'd develop pneumonia.

I stood there shivering and bracing myself against the wind and the rain as it lashed into me, and I looked up and saw a light blue van pull up and a kindly old man lean out. "You going to the ferry with all that baggage?"

I turned back into the rain, and shouted back at him that I was.

"Hop in then, I'm going that way."

I hesitated and remembered the previous night and then thought again. He looked fatherly and kind and he was old, and I'd get even more ill if I stood out in the rain for much longer.

I argued with myself, and then stood there while he jumped out and heaved my case in the front and I climbed in after it, out of the cold.

The van heater was on and I sat there comfortably and let its warmth thaw me out.

He drove slowly along Richmond Terrace and we exchanged polite small talk about the weather, and what I did for a living, and I was looking ahead of me watching the road and then it struck me with a kind of horror that he'd turned off Richmond Terrace and he wasn't heading in the right direction for the ferry anymore.

I went numb with fear. "This way isn't the way to the ferry," I started, somehow hoping that he'd say it was some sort of shorter route.

"I thought I'd take you to see my place," he beamed at me. And the previously kind face of an old man changed into the face of a maniac. Smiling and plotting. . . .
My stomach was churning over and beads of sickly cold sweat came over my face.

The bluff had worked the night before. Would it work now?

"I'd like to see it, but I've got to meet my brother."

"I thought you said you were on your own over here."

I realised what I'd said, and hated myself. "Yes, I am, I mean alone without a husband, but there's my brother, and he's expecting me over, he lives in Manhattan."
He looked at me and looked back to the road; searching for something. A sick feeling in the pit of my stomach grew; would he believe me? "What I'll do," I went on, "is take your phone number and we'll meet tonight or sometime this week for a drink; let me write down your number."

I searched in my bag and pulled out a pen and paper and wrote down the number he reeled off to me hoping he wouldn't see that my hands were shaking so much I couldn't hold the pen.

He stared at me in a searching way. And I looked back at him impassively as I pushed the scrap of paper back into my handbag.

He kept driving, and I still couldn't tell if he was heading in the proper direction.

The driving rain was lashing against the windows of the van, and it gave me a cut-off feeling, as if it was just us, just us and the truck.

I looked round behind me into the back of the van to see what he was carrying. A great big empty van. Nothing. Except for what lay on the floor. Handcuffs. Attached to two long chains bolted securely to the edge of the van. He was talking and I wasn't registering.

"I want a pet y'see. For back there."

He grinned at me. Rotten teeth and dry cracked mouth.

I carried on. "You will be in when I phone, won't you? I've been a bit lonely. I'm glad we've met." I paused. "I like dogs too, so if you're getting a pet that's good isn't it?"

And I was thinking in my mind; Jesus Christ, God please." I was holding my breath for so long, I thought my lungs would burst.

I just kept watching the windscreen wipers as they went backwards and forwards across the windscreen. A long pause. Suddenly, he turned the van completely around and started back in the direction we'd come from. We drew up to the ferry terminal and I still kept the same impassive expression on my face. Until the van came to a halt.

I opened the door, half not believing that he was letting me out, I leaped down and pulled the suitcase after me.

"I'll wait in for you to phone me later," he said and looked at me severely.

I told him I would, then walked off as normally as I could, until I was out of sight in the ferry terminal.

As soon as I got round the corner my legs buckled underneath me; and I leant over the suitcase to ease the dizziness. I was sweating hard and my clothes had partly dried from the van heater and clung to me and smelt of rain and dampness. . . It was then that the emptiness of my stomach forced me to retch uncontrollably. I couldn't stop it. Then after several minutes, it stopped as quickly as it had begun.

I lugged the suitcase along behind me, and boarded the ferry.

I sat downstairs on the lower deck and gazed out the porthole, a drunken old woman approached me, and I moved away, and then watched her as she scavenged among the bins and ate an old biscuit she found amongst the rubbish.

I filed off at South Ferry and took the number one train uptown. I got off at 42nd Street, stupidly. With my interest in The Children of Israel, and that area they spoke in, I forgot that it was a notorious red light area, and the worse place I could have picked.

I collected the money owed to me from Cafe 43 and then looked around for somewhere to stay.

I just wanted somewhere to sleep for the night. Somewhere safe, where I could sleep well to try to shake off the dizziness and the flu, and the effects of everything that I had experienced in the last twenty four hours.

I walked around 44th and 45th Street, pulling my suitcase along behind me, and I was getting dizzier and dizzier by the minute, until I felt as if I could hardly walk another step.

I remembered something as I looked in my handbag to check that the money I'd just picked up was still there; I had some phone numbers people had given me. A girl I'd worked with, the woman on the plane I'd been talking to. Maybe they would know of somewhere.

I went to a phone box, and dialled the number on the first piece of paper. A deep male voice answered, "Oh hello."

He appeared to know me and recognise me by my voice but I didn't recognise his. "It's James."

I thought back, James? James? I didn't know anyone of that name.

"We met in the restaurant."

I still couldn't figure out who it was, but I was getting a picture of a priest or someone like that in my mind.

And then all of a sudden it clicked. The speaker! It was the speaker I had seen on my first day. The one in the red robe. I must have inadvertently jotted the number down on this piece of blank paper.

I was going to say so that other name isn't your real name, when it occurred to me that he probably hadn't meant to let on. Instead I asked him did he know of anywhere to stay cheaply. He said he didn't and then paused.
I said "Oh well then, not to worry. I'm sorry I phoned, I didn't know it was you" and I said goodbye. I felt an infinite sadness as I heard the click at the other end, and I hung up.

I decided to not call the other numbers. All of a sudden it seemed like a stupid idea, and I picked up my suitcase again and made my way back down 44th Street.

I was so tired that I felt I couldn't go on any further. I stopped at the nearest place, that there was a sign up saying 'Vacancies'.

Upstairs in the small hotel, I paid a Puerto Rican forty dollars for the room and he asked me did I want it all night or just for a few hours.

I asked him what he meant, when a coloured girl with an English accent, behind him laughed.

"You're English aren't you, I'd get somewhere else if I were you."

I looked at her and I felt beads of sweat on my upper lip, "I just need somewhere to sleep, please", and I swayed forward.

She walked along with a bunch of keys then showed me into a small dark single room and handed me a key. She closed the door behind her and I was left alone. And I fell onto the bed, and lay there for a long time.
It started to get dark then outside. I'd just remembered I hadn't eaten at all that day, but I didn't have any energy to do anything about that. I just lay there, inert and lonely.

I lay on the bed, staring at the ceiling and then watched the flies buzz around the naked light bulb.

Echoes of laughter came up from the street below; and I sat up on the edge of the bed and I could see myself reflected in the mirror that was perched on the chest of drawers.

I looked awful. Dyed hair. Black roots again. Dark circles under my eyes and a pale damp face wet with perspiration.

What was I doing.? Who was I? What had I done to end up like this? Oh God, what had I done to end up like this?

This. This was me. A nothing. A no-one. Alone in a room. And what if I took a rope and tied it to that light bulb and then stood on the bed and tied it around my neck and then jumped, who would care who would know who I was? I was no-one!

A no-one girl died today. Who cares? She didn't matter. Like it doesn't matter when you swat a fly.
I didn't matter. There was no-one else on the whole planet who knew of me, or would cry if in the morning the black girl would unlock the door to see why I hadn't handed back the key and find the body swinging there with the flies buzzing around it. And the police would come and cut it down. "Who was she?" . . . . . She was no-one."

I lay back on the bed again and tried to sleep. A cockroach crawled out of a hole in the mattress and ran up my face. I jumped up in horror and looked down at the bed, where I'd been lying. Hundreds of tiny black cockroaches came pouring out of the tiny hole and ran across the bed.

I leapt up and yanked the mattress of the bed and turned it up to flip it over. As I held it in the air I could see underneath; the distinctive flimsy pink rubber of contraceptives stared up at me, about twenty of them. Hidden under the mattress and glistening with stinking semen, all used.
I flung the mattress down and gagged on the smell and I propped myself up on the floor underneath the window, breathing deeply to take in the night air and eradicate the growing stench all around me.

I reached over to my handbag to check the 30 dollars I had left was still there, and I was rooting through my bag, when I saw it. The letter from Ian Brady I'd nearly thrown away at the airport, and I re-read it, lying there, and I felt a strange kind of feeling as I read it. It kept saying things like I don't think I deserve to have a daughter like you, and, how he was looking forward to hearing from me, and take care of yourself, at the end. Take care, care.

He had no family. No relatives. He'd broke off with his foster family years ago. And I wondered who did he turn to when there is no-one? Who was it he pictured in his mind hugging him when he felt down and lost and scared? - Did he think of me? Was I his saviour now, as he had been mine? I knew for all the world that he was thinking of me at that very moment.

And what about everyone else? What did they do? Who did they go running to? Who was on the other end of their piece of string as they flew around the world. Who came to them in the darkness?...Where, oh where was the one at the end of my piece of string?

Years ago and in what seemed like another lifetime I would've prayed to God, but now I didn't understand him or know him anymore, and he seemed miles away.

The contrast of the warmth of his letter and the coldness of this new country, seemed enormous. I pulled out a note-pad I had in my bag and a pen, and I began to write.

Wouldn't that guarantee me for the rest of my life, that there would always be someone? There'd always be a letter with 'take care' on the end, and in the darkness of that room, that night, I made a decision. It would be him. He would be there for me. Just like he always had been. . . . .

It was all I had left . . . .

————————

214

The next few days passed in a blur. I remember coming in and out of consciousness and that hotel owner coming in and asking me for more money. And then him shouting at me telling me to get out.

I remember vaguely struggling with my case onto the subway and the number one train downtown to South Ferry. And then phoning Joe, my old landlord. I had no more money and I was ill. But he was my last hope.

I fell asleep near the phone box in the ferry terminal. And the next thing, awoke to the smell of leather pushed up against my face. I opened my eyes and saw Joe's face; red, bloodshot eyes and pale pallor.

He lifted me and I clung onto the leather lapels of his jacket as he carried me out to his car and lay me down on the back seat.

Then I watched the back of his head, strong and safe as the car moved and the street lights shining in on my face lulled me and I closed my eyes and passed out.

Joe took me back to 1836 Richmond Terrace and my tiny attic room. It was about two weeks before I recovered and he lent me some money and saw that I had enough food to last me before he flew down to his other house in Virginia Beach, where his wife and children lived.

Joe told me he'd fit extra locks on to the repaired front door and told me to not go out after dark unless I had to and especially not near Port St George.

I was nervous about being there again but it was the only choice I had. I still had some deposit to clear that I'd paid Joe when I'd moved in and he said I could pay him back the money he'd left me as soon as I got a job.

I worked then. I'd go backwards and forwards over to Manhattan and 51st

Street and Broadway where I'd got a job in a restaurant as a waitress again. It was quite a nice place, where all the theatre goers would come after the show and have drinks and supper. I'd work there from 3 o'clock in the afternoon round to 11 o'clock at night and then head straight for South Ferry to catch the ferry back to Staten Island. The pay was bad, but the tips were good, and I soon became financially independent again. I even began to face food again.

I remember in South Ferry where I'd wait to board the ferry various homeless characters would lay along the benches sleeping, and every night a policeman would come round with a truncheon and whack it down on the side of the bench to wake them up.

Then he'd shout at them to move on.

There was no need for the callousness and it was unbearable to watch these people; all solitary figures, alone and homeless, with no-one and nowhere to go. Shuffle out the door of the ferry terminal out into the cold and onto the streets in their separate loneliness, each going in different directions to find another bench, another box, another alley.

Time passed and eventually it was Christmas. I lay on my bed in the attic room in the darkness and listened to the Christmas carols on the Radio, all my favourites, Silent Night, O Little Town of Bethlehem. And I thought back to other Christmases and other places. Christmas in the orphanage and Christmas in a hundred other rooms and a thousand other places.

They say that people who are alone at this time of year feel the pain more keenly and that many people alone kill themselves because they cannot bear that pain.

It is a time for families, not a time for people like me, and it makes us ashamed and want to hide, and pretend we didn't exist and we hope that it passes quickly so we don't have to watch the others with their happiness and their love. Hoping it passes quickly so we can pretend that everyone is like ourselves in tiny rooms listening to the Christmas carols on the radio and imagining that there may come a time in the future when we too will be one of the lucky ones; the ones with arms full of presents to give to others. And the ones round the big table on Christmas day with faces full of love and belonging . . . and a family . . . .

And I went and stood by the window and looked out at the boats, their strange lights making their way over to the island in the darkness and I'd wonder who was on them, and whether on one of them was someone like me, alone tonight. I closed my eyes and prayed for them that they did not feel the pain as intensely as I. No-one should ever be that alone.

Christmas passed and then it was New Years Eve and then a new year. 1988.

All the excitement died down and everything had got back to normal and I went to and from work as usual.

The snow was really deep in January and it piled high up most of the steps leading to the house, and I had to buy some wellington boots to wade through the snow.

The temperatures were still below freezing and after work I'd mainly spend my time huddled under blankets reading a book, or trying to stuff blankets and things in the tops of the windows where they were broken and a draught would blow in. I felt very empty around then, and I lived in a very robotic sort of way, concentrating mainly on working to feed myself to make sure I didn't get sick again.

And it was one day in early January when everything changed. It was an ordinary morning and I'd just gone out the door. I was making my way down

217

the front garden to the gate at the end, and it was taking me ages, I had to wade nearly knee high through all the snow, and I was wrapped up in so many scarves I could barely see where I was going.

I calculated I had about three minutes to get to the bus-stop which was a hundred yards down the road before I missed the bus to the ferry which came every half an hour.

As I neared the gate Joe, the old blackman who was sweeping the snow off the porch called out to me.

"English, there's a letter for you."

"What d'you mean?" I shouted back, "I don't know anyone."

I wrinkled my nose in annoyance. He had to be wrong, and he was going to make me late.

"It's from England too," he stopped sweeping and left on his broom to look at me. I ran up the steps and past him back into the dusty little kitchen. And there amongst the other letters lay a long blue air mail envelope. All the way from England, and addressed to me. And the handwriting on the front looked disturbingly familiar. Postmark Liverpool. Sender, Ian Brady.

I picked it up, then leapt down the steps, skidded on some ice and fell straight down into a pile of snow. I got up and dusted the snow down just in time to watch the bus to the ferry speed past the end of the garden.

Joe stood on the steps and rocked to and fro with laughter, "I guess the letter was worth it."

I'd forgotten the letter for a moment and as I looked down it lay in the snow before me and I smiled up at him.

"It's from my family in England."

"Oh who's that then?" he enquired.

I hesitated then said it without thinking "my father."

When I look back now it seems a stupid thing to have said, but way back then it seemed sort of natural.

And everyone in the house knew that when the long blue air mail letters came addressed to me, that they were from my family, miles away in England and they'd keep a look out for me when I came in from work, tired and shivering from the cold and looking miserable.

Joe would sometimes stand in the kitchen and watch me sort through the mail and find nothing and then get on with making some soup or something to take it up to my room, pretending not to care; and then he'd stand there and smile and say, maybe it came in the late post and it's still in the mail box by the gate; so I'd have to wade through the snow to the small grey mail box we had for number 1836. And sure enough there it'd be, where Joe had put it squashed in the back of the box. He'd nearly always do that and he said it was because in case he missed me when I first saw it, because he never saw me smile, and it was only when one of those blue letters came, that he said I smiled and he told me it made him happy because a young girl should be always smiling.

It may seem stupid now for someone to become happy over just a letter. But not to me, not then. It was from someone who knew me, someone who knew me before I became the solitary girl who lived in the attic and didn't talk to anyone much, a time before the hardness of living the hand to mouth existence that I did in that strange cold city. Someone, the only one, who cared whether I lived or died.

His letters came regularly then; all through the winter and through into

February when the weather started to get better. And on some days a watery sun lit up the thin layer of frost that covered everything, and if you screwed up your eyes you could pretend to yourself that Spring was nearly here and the living would be a lot easier than it had been.

I was still working in Manhattan, and I'd get the 8.00 ferry in the mornings; sometimes I'd catch the early post, and I'd have a letter from England to read whilst standing on the forward deck, the wind nearly whipping it out of my hand as we sailed into Manhattan or, on Saturdays, my day off, I'd go and walk down to Greenwich Village and along St Mark's Place and into one of the bars along there, and I'd sit at a table in the corner, and I'd take with me a notebook and pen, and I'd write to him about the the coldness of the city I was living in and the toughness and the loneliness of my life. I told him about the streets of New York and what they were like, and what it was like to walk down them. The tall, overbearing buildings, 5th Avenue and Park Avenue, filled with shops containing stuff so expensive and sophisticated that they wouldn't look out of place in the boudoir of a queen, every luxury that one could imagine, and trimmed with gold, and scented with the finest perfumes. And then outside the shops in the streets sat the poor, begging in the kerbs, the mostly black bodies, wrapped inadequately with blankets to keep out the cold; mothers with their babies in their arms and small children at their feet, sitting at the steps of the subway station, hands raised as in the position of prayer but open in the position of begging to the disinterested figures who tripped by in their long warm coats, who didn't see them. The hungry eyes blinded from the dazzle of the gold and the finery in the window displays of the beautiful shops, and upon the more comfortable and wealthy New Yorkers who had jobs and warm places to live.

There was a young black boy who I'd see at Times Square, 42nd Street subway, and he'd always be standing on the steps wrapped in an old dirty mustard coloured blanket. He was only about fifteen or so, and he'd stand there shivering or jumping up and down to keep warm or engulfed in his worn covering with his head down, trying to sleep. I kept going past him, and it happened that twice I didn't have any money to give him. And he'd look at me, and I always had my big, warm coat on, that I'd bought in England before all the trouble, and I knew it looked expensive and he probably thought I lived in a big house and had lots of money. But he'd just smile at me. He'd smile and say "A smile from you, just warms me more that anything could: God has blessed you with a pretty smile, and you can be anyone you want to be."

And I'd wonder how did he smile? How did he smile when he stood there day after day the cold biting through to his bones? And how could he talk of God, how could he talk of God when God had been so forgetting of him, so harsh to him?

If you turn your face from something, you can sometimes pretend it's not there; and I was just the same as everybody else; And so I turned the other way.

I turned, but there again, it faced me.

An old woman lay face down in the women's toilet of the ferry terminal at South Ferry. She was an old tramp, and she lay in a puddle of her own urine, a half eaten biscuit in her hand, and groaning. She stunk to high heaven and all the women who came in to the women's room ignored her; she was a tramp, a bag lady, she smelt and she was repulsive and it didn't matter. And when the horn sounded for the ferry, we all filed on board with not a thought for the old woman lying there. Yet, me, I was there too. And after a few minutes on the boat, my mind had again filled with my own worries and my aspirations, and she no longer existed.

Sometimes, I'd come home at night and I'd lie up in my room huddled under the blankets, and I'd write to him, and I'd wonder, who was God, when he let people suffer so much, and I'd ask him 'Who is God? Is he real? Who are we and what is it that we are doing here?'

And one night as I lay in my room just on the point of falling asleep, I heard screams coming from outside and a car screeching and I rushed to the window in fright and there I saw a man standing against a wall near the house. A car was ramming into his legs again and again, and I heard the sickening horror of his screams, until they got fainter and fainter and he crumpled to the ground into a dark puddle of his own blood. And I stood in the window, horrified, and watched as the men got out of the car, lifted up his body and put it in the back of the car and got back in as nonchalantly as if they were loading a case of beer.

The engine started and the car headlights lit up and I ducked down below the window-sill in case the light shone up to the window and they saw me watching them. I slid down into a seating position there underneath the window in the darkness and I cried, and tried to imagine what it would be like to have a car run into my legs over and over again, until the bone splintered knowing I was permanently crippled, just before I passed out. And I wondered what would become of the man now. Would he be beaten again, or was he dead already, to be flung in a ditch somewhere. No-one caring.

And I wrote to him and I told him of the misery and I asked him, "Why is a man like a wolf to another man? Why does one person take pleasure in the destruction of another? Why is there evil? Why did evil have to be invented?"

Time went on, and living continued, until one day, when I was walking down 5th Avenue and heading home after a day's work handing out leaflets. I'd bought a bagel and I was chewing on it and a man with fair hair lay in the street, crawling along the floor, trying to grab on to the legs of passers by. He was screaming "Help me. Help me." And everyone walked past him.

And so did I. Head down and pulling my coat around me to keep warm. I felt nothing until I got home, and flung myself on the bed and cried.
I felt that everywhere there was ugliness, all around there was cold, no warmth, no laughter, no peace, and worst of all, no love.

It was like an icyness was coming up inside me. An icy cruel hardness that was telling me to not care, to harden myself against the sights I was seeing, and to not let them move me in any way.

And I resolved to kill myself before I got to the point when the suffering didn't make me cry. To let God take me before my heart toughened up like leather, and I no longer felt any pain. But someone, somewhere must have answered my prayer, because instead of getting harder and the icy iron bar inside me expanding, it suddenly vanished and I was left with a feeling of emptyness inside, like someone had cut off all my energy. And the feeling of being different from others, and the strong isolation of unreality became stronger.

Until in the end it was like being stuck on top of a monopoly board, and forced to play the game over and over, until it made you nauseous. And you realised it was a game that went on until you had aged enough that you were ready to die. A never ending pointless, futile game. And all the other pieces had smiles on their faces, all except for one piece that had tears flowing down its face, with the knowledge that there was no big hand around to make sure that the game didn't become nasty and vicious, in the efforts to be the one that won; with all the pushing and the shoving and the clamouring for the ultimate prizes.

I didn't want to live in the world, people had all of a sudden taken on the appearance of machines. The way they were living seemed so wrong it seemed so far from God. And yet they were so powerful, they were so sure that they were right, and they were in the majority. So they must be.

I felt as if I was going out of my mind. Mad to cry all the time and worry about why we were here and where God was. I had never felt I belonged, I'd always felt different to the others. But now, well it was as if what had made me different was somehow getting stronger. And I was getting more and more detached from it all. Each day, it became more unreal, and the people, like grotesque puppets. And they seemed to me to be somehow like animals or nonsensical. I felt as if somehow I knew more than they did, as if I could see clearer, but I didn't know what it was that I could see . . . . All I knew then was that it frightened me. I seemed to be losing my hold on everything and reality seemed to be fading from me, and I was trapped alone in some sort of goldfish bowl, cut off from my feelings, cut off from everything. Alone inside my head .

It seemed that there was no-one else in the world like me. I was different, and I had no-one I could confide the pain to and terror of feeling the way I did. I think it took me a long time to realise, back then. I think I just saw him as a friend; someone that I was grateful to for being there and listening to me, when I was so alone. And it was slowly that I realised, with his letters that became less formal and less restricted and more open, more relaxed. It was very slowly that I realised that in some way, and somehow, Ian was exactly the same kind as I was, and like me he'd been there since birth. The not belonging, the feeling different; and the alienation from other people.

And we talked. We talked in the way two Englishmen would talk if they came across each other after one had been many years in a foreign land.

After many years putting up with the pidgeon English, the alienation and the feeling of not belonging. There was someone else's face looking back from the loneliness of my own reflection, and it was his.

He remembered his childhood as one of great pain. It mattered then, he'd said, being a bastard, fostered out to another family because his own mother didn't want him. He told me that he always pretended not to care, but it had mattered and it had mattered a great deal. He'd thought that the family who he had been living with had been his own, until they told him that that is where she had left him, the place where she had carried him as a baby, when he was only a few months old . . . .just like me.

"I didn't think that was the reason for it though. I always thought everyone felt that way. Strange and dreamy and forever retreating into a world inside yourself, until you realised that they were not like you; you were of some different kind. And you felt like you didn't belong, you didn't belong in this world, and it was somehow wrong, and stupid like a dream that you had woken up to. Even the child's games in the playground had seemed futile to me and I had stood alone at the edge of the crowds, never fitting in and always alone. And then when I was older, I'd found it hard to accept the values of others. It seemed futile and pointless, their living, like trying to obtain something in a dream. I felt as if I was awake, and they were asleep. Later on, the feelings had got stronger and stronger, then by the time I was seventeen or eighteen, everything started to become increasingly unreal. People seemed like puppets and marionettes. Their lives cotton wool, marshmallow, unreal. Thats when, well, that was the beginning of the end for me! . . . . .

"That is when it began to get dangerous."

February ended, and made way for March, and it was still minus 2 and bitterly cold and the snow was still visible on the ground.

I was still working going backwards and forwards to Manhattan, and hurrying home in the evenings to get in and huddle beneath the blankets and keep warm.

I'd taken to pampering myself with a cup of hot chocolate and brandy, and more often than not Frankie and Joe would catch me in the kitchen boiling up the milk and they'd stand there in the cold kitchen shivering in their tatty old dressing gowns and eye the bottle of brandy on the kitchen table, so in the end I'd make three extra cups, and go round and knock on everybody's door with some hot drinks, and then it got such a big thing that I'd do it regularly at eleven o'clock every night. And I felt like Wendy and the lost boys, and they seemed kind of lost, all over sixty and no family any of them, just their tiny rooms, their tiny rooms that they hardly ever came out of.

I spent most evenings writing to Ian and I'd laughed and mocked his last letter. "It's been freezing temperatures over here, and I'm huddled up in bed, drinking a huge cup of hot chocolate and reading over your cryptic letter. I'm sorry for laughing, but you spoke of danger. I can't see any danger. What danger?"

And then the reply.

"But that's just it, you can't see it!"

And then one night, one night when I'd been reading quite late I'd just turned out the tiny bedside lamp and I was lying there in the darkness, I heard some kind of tapping, like tapping on the window, and I got straight out of bed and looked outside to see if I could see anything; but I couldn't, and then I saw a branch that was quite near the window and I thought 'Oh that must have been it', but it didn't sound like a branch, it sounded like urgent knocking, tapping, like someone was trying to get in.

I lay back down to sleep and I was just about to drop off when I felt a kind of shaking, like a trembling, like the house was rocking and I leapt out of bed, terrified and ran straight down to Joe's room on the next floor and banged hard on the door.

I heard rustlings then eventually Joe's face appeared round the door and he looked me up and down strangely, until I realised I only had a flimsy T-shirt on.

I tugged the T-shirt down over my knees and looked at him impassively "Joe did you feel the earthquake?"
"This is New York, not California, and no I haven't felt a thing, I was fast asleep."

I looked at him in surprise, "Well, I just felt a really huge tremor as if the whole house was shaking and rocking. Maybe if a huge truck just went past, do you think that was it?" He assured me that it must have been that, but that it was an old house, and secure in its foundations and he had never known it in all the time he had lived there to ever rock or shake. I stood there staring at him hoping he'd say he'd come up and check my room to see if everything was alright, but he didn't, he just said goodnight and closed the door again. I made my way back upstairs and got back into bed. I left my bedside light on then: I felt scared, I hate it when something happens not knowing what's causing it, or what it is, and I definitely had felt the rocking and shaking.

It must've been a good ten minutes later when I was just lying there, wondering whether it would happen again, when it did. The rocking and the shaking and I sat up in bed and looked around me and then looked down and I realised in horror that it wasn't the house at all, that was shaking, but the bed, and not really the bed - just the mattress on it.

I sat up in fright, a deep clammy cold feeling of fear coming over me, and I sat watching the mattress waiting to see if it would move again.

And I was sitting up on the bed staring out into the dimly lit room when I heard a loud whisper coming from the corner of the room; it came from the direction of the dark crucifix that hung there. And I sat there hardly daring to breathe in case I missed it again. Surely I must be imagining things.
I felt a deep terror deep inside. I'd heard a whisper. Loud and yet soft, as if it had come from out of the air, somehow.

And I sat up all that night, straining into the darkness trying to see some sort of sign that there was something in my room; but I could see nothing. It wasn't long after that that I felt as if some sort of veil had been lifted or some sort of door had opened. And after that I began to see and hear things that no-one else could.

That was when I knew that I had gone mad. Lost, alone, with no money in a strange cold city and I had gone mad. I'd end up on the street. I knew I'd end up on the street like the others. Homeless; like the woman who lay in the toilets in the ferry terminal face down in her own urine, a mad, lonely old lady, to remain forever outside respectable society.

I couldn't sleep at night because of them. All of them on at me all at once, they'd fill my room as soon as it got dark, so I'd sleep with the light on all the time, and be filled with terror if I ever forgot and left it off.

They wouldn't let me sleep, on and on tormenting me, telling me of what was going to happen to me, a lonely death alone in a room, swinging from a lampshade; they seemed to know my fears, to somehow hear my thoughts and they laughed at me and mocked me until I'd put my hand over my mouth to stop myself from screaming, and turn my face and bury it into the pillow, sobs racking my body; and I'd press my hands up to my ears, and then they'd start off at me from inside, echoes of laughter, a hundred of them, all at once, all straining to make me listen like a mini transistor inside my skull, with the volume turned up too far so I couldn't think my own thoughts, just theirs. I'd have these thoughts in my head that weren't mine, horrible thoughts, thoughts from some black pit of pornography or vicious sadistic 'pleasures' they called it; all shown on a television screen inside my head. Was this what Ian Brady had gone through all those years ago?

And then it wasn't only at nights, they were with me always, telling me things during the day, until I couldn't talk to anyone without them interrupting inside my head. Until I had hardly any room in my head for my thoughts, and I felt reality had rocked and rolled and somehow I had slipped off.

I didn't know whether to tell him at first; he was all I had. If I lost him, I'd drown, and I had to keep afloat. And I left it as long as I could. I left it until I'd started to see silhouettes in everything, outlines on objects and lines in the air like I could see the atmosphere.

And then it was too hard to get out of bed in the morning; the energy supply had been turned off again, and I sat up in the bed and stared out into space listening to them, on and on. Until I told him that I understood if he never wrote back to me 'Who wants a friend that has gone insane?' I'd asked him.

The week that I waited for a reply was the longest. I wished, in that time that I had never told him. I was sure I had lost him and he was the only connection to reality that I had.

And I remember when I did get it, I ripped it open, and let tears run down my face as I read it. Everything would be alright now and it seemed strange, as if I was me long ago; the nights in the orphanage in the dark, whispering up to the picture above my bed, all my innermost secrets, confiding everything and being accepted. Wanting and begging for the unconditional love of my family.

'Whatever you do, whatever you say, I will always be there for you.' It was all I ever wanted really.
I had the strength then, and I went and got myself another job, and whenever 'they' pushed me too much, shouted at me all at once inside my head, I'd block them out. 'Medication and pills work as blocks, they give me that here, it can be done without medication . . . .' Ian wrote this to me . . . .

Suddenly everything was easier, I could cope with it all; and not only that, it was as if I'd tapped into something inside of him, because all of a sudden I'd made contact with some sort of part of him that he had previously kept to himself, and I felt that any barriers that were there had totally disappeared and I was free, free to confide and talk and tell him absolutely everything, and I did, I told him it all.

And the letters that went backwards and forwards became almost like a dream themselves; like some sort of unreality, part of the other world, part of the world where 'they' came from. Had a stranger picked them up and read them, they would have seemed bizarre, crazy. It was as if we belonged to another world, and so spoke a different language. And he'd been there longer than I had, so I needed teaching.

"Destroy this"; he'd put on the end of all the letters, and yet I'd kept some of them. Anything where he'd spoke about our world, I'd destroyed them. I'd not want to keep it lying around in case anyone read them. I wanted no-one to know. I had to beware of others he'd told me. "It's like us and them. They're not the same," he wrote.

He'd destroyed all my letters as he'd read them; no-one would ever see them. *"Remember the parable of Mektoub,"* he'd said, *"Mektoub was a great wrestler in ancient times. He taught a particular student 300 holds. One day the pupil felt confident enough to challenge Mektoub to a match. They wrestled and Mektoub won. The pupil was indignant and said "You never taught me that last hold." Mektoub replied "Just because I love you and I trust you did you think I was a complete fool." In short, always keep a final hold in reserve and if disloyalty occurs you use it.*

It was some kind of strange friendship, but back then, back in the madness it was all a part of my life.

The letters that went backwards and forwards, where he taught and I listened.

He wrote:-
"I think that we are all minds out of control. The controller is the higher self; then when you first begin to be aware of this, i.e. the higher self awakes and shines its light into the mind, you start to see that the world created by the other minds (the still asleep minds) is unreal to you.

The next stage is where you relate more to your higher self, your consciousness has moved up into the higher self and you watch your mind and you are living but you feel detached from it, as if it isn't you - and you're right it isn't.

You start to behave differently from then on: all their petty loves and desires and rules land unions like marriage and their hopes and dreams. Well you can see how petty it all is, how they invest all their energies in a stupid dream. You feel superior to them after that, you can't help it . Hide it. Don't let them see you're different. They'll call you insane, try to get you locked away.

People called my a psychopath, ever since I was seventeen. All a psychopath is, is someone whose higher ego is awake. It realises the attachments and sentimental affections of the mind are all petty illusion so it does not have them;
It is then called by the still asleep minds who are in the majority, and judged by them as being calloused, but it is not calloused, it is just different from them. It realises, it sees deeper.

The so-called psychopath normally ends up a killer because as he is awake, the higher self shines down, and you see the light is too strong, the energy is too much, like a power, too much power, and it forms tensions in the head, like bursts in your head. The tension makes them kill, they have to learn how to control it. I did. I went through that stage and I controlled it. You will go through it too. Talk to me about it, I'll help you control it. It's just a stage you see, you have to keep going.

You told me you thought that you were going mad. There is no such thing as mad. Insanity is just lost in a world that we know nothing of, we are lost, not insane. There is, shall we say, like a path, you must try to stick to it.

Our minds (our instruments we have to work with) are so inadequate compared to the higher self, they are like childrens' toys in comparison - easily broken and weak.

231

It wakes up from the illusion and it doesn't know where it is; it doesn't know what is happening - It is like a child then, in its vulnerability - A child because it is functioning in a different world that it has just entered. A different world a different consciousness. You have me, where when I was your age, I had no-one. You won't get lost. We're the same kind. I will help you.

You say you feel compelled to do things. Always a compulsion. The higher self impresses upon you, you cannot resist it, you are compelled to do its bidding. Compared to the mind, the higher self is incomparable in strength. One is a God, the other is a weak child. You are just compelled to do its will, then you try to philosophise and reason why you are doing the things that you do - And you try to work out a philosophy.

You say that you feel guided to certain books that seem to rationalise what you are doing. I read De Sade, Nietzsche, Dostoevsky, through them I tried to reason with myself, about what I was doing. But I could never've stopped myself. I tried to rationalize it to myself or I would've lost sight of reality and lost myself forever.

I feared insanity and as this world was unreal to me, and I was compelled to do the things that I did, I had to reason some sort of philosophy. My higher self guided me to the books that I read. It helped me, to find reason in my actions . . . . Ian."

And I was getting the letters and I was having dreams, and it was then that I had that dream. It had started with a long path. A long dark pathway covered in snow and a dark foreboding forest either side. And I started walking down it, and I saw his footprints there in the snow, so I followed them, and trod in them. Feeling safe knowing he was before me. Until his footprints trailed off and I lost track of them and I had to forge on and make my own. And it got darker and more frightening. And furry creatures and winged insects brushed past me touching against my face. Moths with huge wings and eyes yellow and glowing in the dark. And then I heard a noise behind me and I turned and as I did, I saw it.

232

A large round transparent column and inside the column was a man. I walked up to it. And to my horror it was him. Ian was inside it. As if frozen in a column of ice. And he seemed as if he was asleep. And there was an expression of suffering, and endurance on his face that made me want to smash the ice, to smash it and get to him.

And I stood back, stood back and looked at it. The great big glass column with him inside it. And I heard a voice talking to me, in the dream, reciting some sort of poem. And it reminded me of a children's story I'd read in the orphanage when I was very young.

The voice urged me on and I kept on walking and walking. At the side of the path were other paths leading off and I could see beautiful scenery and castles and palaces at the beginnings of them, and hear laughter and merriment and people enjoying themselves.

And I walked on and on until I grew more despairing, it seemed never ending and it seemed like I'd never get there. And I felt stupid for not taking one of the other paths off and resting, as most of the others had done. And I began to think I must be mad, stupid, crazy and all my hopes were the hopes of a madman.

And then just as I was about to give up, it started to get warmer, then warmer still. And then I saw it. The light.

And I dreamt I found it. I found home. Our home and all the others. The unwanted, the losers, the misfits and the lonely and I turned round and I called to him and I could see him running wildly towards me. And I grabbed him by the hand and dragged him with me and he was crying and I was crying. And God welcomed him home and looked down on everybody with the love of a Father. And behind us there were shouts and cries of joy as everyone followed us into this world, this home.

And everybody holding each other and blending together under a light stronger and warmer than the sun.

When I awoke, I lay and sobbed at the reality that I was no longer there but here, a girl in a room with no-one but you.

And I remembered straight away the poem that the voice had recited to me in the dream.

"For that he was a spirit too delicate to carry
out their earthly and abhorred commands,
Refusing their grand hests, they did confine him,
By help of their most potent ministers.
And in their most unmitigable rage,
Into a cloven pine, within which Rift,
Imprisoned he didst painfully remain . . ."

It was Shakespeare's Tempest and I remembered it from a children's book I'd read 'A Wrinkle in Time' where a little boy is a different kind from everybody else, and the difference makes him vulnerable, and he is overcome by dark forces that controlled his mind and drove him to evil.

I found a copy of the book in an old occult book shop on 53rd Street and I sent it to him.

It was two weeks later that I found an old battered copy of 'Goethes Faust' in the mail box at the end of the garden.

"They promised me a redemption, I do it favours and it does me favours."

The days passed, then the days flowed into the weeks and the weeks months. The summer came in New York, and it was the hottest weather that I have ever known. People were packed like sardines into the subways during rush hours, and numerous fights would break out caused by the unbearable stuffiness and the heat of the underground, making everyone short tempered.

I got a tan, and I sent him some photos; Times Square, in the hot summer months, full with tourists and pulsating with music and the smell of hot dogs cooling in the air, and the hot over-heating tarmac on the roads and the petrol fumes from the jam packed traffic hold-ups.

I'd go down to St Marks Place a lot and sit in 'Grass Roots' or I'd walk around Greenwich Village looking in the shops and the street markets at the antiques. I'd walk into the bars and sit there of a Friday or Saturday night, when I could bear the loneliness no longer, and I'd sometimes strike up a conversation with someone. Always a man and always they would want to sleep with me. Even once I was mistaken for a prostitute, as I sat at the bar eyeing the others thoughtfully, in the hope that for a time the drink and their slurred conversation could make me forget that I was alone.

I'd meet other girls while I was working and I'd watch them laughing with each other and arranging to meet each other at each others' house, and at parties, yet I'd blush and stammer if they ever spoke to me for too long or paid me too much attention. I felt that they'd see through the mask, see what I really was, and I didn't even know myself what I really was; but I knew I was different enough that I had to hide it. How could I be a part of their world, mix with them, when I felt so very differently, when I knew and saw what they didn't.

Apart from him, there was no-one.

I got scared then, I kept having this strange fear that I might lose him, I'd become utterly dependent on him, as the only thing that was tangible in the strange other world that I seemed to be floating around in. I couldn't have beared to lose him. I began to spend a lot of time in my room trying to think of ways to involve him in something, that would make sure that he would never leave me, or make him tied to me, somehow.

One of those times, when I lay there plotting and planning, the phone started ringing down in the hall. It was Phil Hall.

"Was I talking to Ian?"

I stood there silent on the other end of the phone. I didn't want to speak to him, and I went to replace the receiver when I heard Ted Hynd's voice "Christine, come on, I know you're there. Aren't you going to talk to your Uncle Ted?"

The sound of his voice warmed me, and made me feel sad at the same time. He belonged to a different time and place and I wanted him to hug me, and tell me that I was just in the middle of some awful dream and everything would be alright. He sounded awfully English, compared to the American accents I'd been hearing constantly, and I couldn't help myself from smiling.

"Now come on and tell me what's going on between you and Ian Brady," he coaxed, "We know that there's lots of air mail letters going backwards and forwards; our insiders always keep us informed. Have you asked him whether or not he's going to do the blood test?"

"No I haven't" I snapped back, annoyed that he hadn't even bothered to ask me how I was. "He's all I've got Ted and I need him, I don't want anybody mucking things up."

"Oh come on now," laughed Ted, "you expect me to believe Ian Brady's your best friend, a 23 year old girl and a 50 year old mass murderer. What would

236

you have in common, if you weren't related?

I told him I had nothing to tell him. He continued to press me, then I replaced the receiver and went back upstairs to my room, an idea beginning to form in my mind.

Of course. Ian has said he was my father, but had suggested the blood test. So I began to include in my letters things that couldn't help but move him. How I'd always wanted a father to look up to and lean on, how I'd always felt the need for a family. I didn't make it up, I just drew on my experience. I wanted to push him, to make him say that he'd take the blood test.

He wrote *"There are no provisions in prison for random blood tests."*
Then I had it planned that if he told me his blood group, I'd pretend mine was the same and he'd believe then for good that I was his real daughter and I'd have him then forever. A proper family; but it never happened.

His answer broke my heart. <u>Quote!</u> *"Now you can deny me whenever you wish. If I did and you told the press and everybody else one way or the other, you would be stuck with me for good"*

Autumn vanished in a cloud of golds and greens and the air got colder and once again it was winter time. It's funny, out of all the seasons, winter always seemed to be with us, with summer always seeming to flash by in a week or two, but winter with its relentless chills and drab greyness and painful festivities like Christmas and my birthday seeming to be ever present.

The snow hadn't come yet but it was already freezing winter 1988. I'd usually spend my days in a circle of work and sleep, sleep and work until the constant drudgery threatened to drive me into the ground and everything seemed pointless. None of it would ever end. I'd not had a letter from him that week but I was becoming concerned again that my only company was a letter, weekly, from him, miles away. I stood outside on the ferry, returning from work and watching the bright lit-up Manhattan Island getting smaller and smaller.

I leant over the edge of the ferry and looked into the blackness of the water and sobbed heavily. So much time alone. Too much time alone. Just the letters and it wasn't enough. Not nearly enough. I leant right over the edge of the boat, there was no-one else on deck. Would the water blot out my misery? It would feel cold at first but then numb me totally, so I couldn't feel any more of the endless heavy weight of pain.

I was staring into the sea and the wind was whipping the hair against my face, and making the loose strands cling to the wet streaks my tears had made. If only, oh, if only. If Ian were free, and out here; I wouldn't be so alone.

And then you were there. Tall and dark and staring out to sea; thick overcoat on and the wind blowing your hair, this way and that. I looked up and squinted my eyes against the wind.

"Look at the way the water lashes up against the side of the boat, and the water looks like it is dancing." You were staring back at the island. Then down at the water and somehow you looked excited, "How good it feels to see all this."

238

I looked around me, as if with new eyes. The water looked beautiful, but I hadn't been seeing, because you were there with me. White spray like sea horses cascading out from the back of the boat, high, high into the air. The tears had gone and I turned, and so had you.

Sometimes, just as I was about to fall asleep I saw him. He'd be sitting in the chair at the end of my bed, looking at me before I fell off to sleep. Watching me. Like he had when I was small, from the head of my bed. Then after a while he sat in the chair at the side of my bed, legs covered with a dark red coloured blanket; looking out the window at the boats coming into the island. He'd stay, until I fell asleep. Then vanish.

Everyone at work knew I lived with my father, who was housebound, and that I was devoted to him and spent all my time with him. That was why, they said, I never had time to mix with anyone. 'That's all she ever thinks about, her father. I think he lives with her, just him and her together in some old house'.
Times Square was as rushed as ever, people bustled along in and out of shops. Christmas carols poured out from loud speakers, and endless figures dressed up as Santa Claus shook collection boxes in front of you round every corner.

I walked along 43rd Street towards Park Avenue and I passed a man playing a guitar, surrounded by a small crowd. He was singing a love song, and lovers watched, their arms entwined around each other and I smiled to myself and felt warm and happy and strong somehow. Their love seemed to give me hope.

I was browsing in all the shops, and I'd seen just what it was that I'd been looking for in an old antique jewellery shop. It was silver and old, like a pocket watch. On the lid there were five small emeralds. It was an old Jewish man in the shop and he told me he'd try to keep it for me if I wanted it, and he let me hold it and examine it. A hundred and fifty dollars. There was no way I could afford it. And yet it was Christmas, I'd had to get him something.
My waitress wages barely covered food and rent, I had nothing left over;

barely enough for stamps and writing paper. Yet I had to have it. I couldn't get it out of my mind. I had to someway show him how important he was to me. He couldn't have Christmas day with nothing, it was bad enough that I had to.

A hundred and fifty dollars. There must be a way. And I kept thinking about it until it obsessed me and I wouldn't rest until I had it wrapped up and posted off just in time for Christmas Day. It'd be something he could keep forever.

I saw the advertisement in the paper. Waitresses in a night club. The money was good and I wondered why. I decided to keep my day job and do this at the weekends until I'd saved enough for the watch.

The nightclub was lit up in a phosphorescent violet blue. The manager's face was an even, suntanned, wrinkled fifty. He had greying hair and a greedy, evil look in his eye that suggested an aptitude for shady dealing in the business world.

He seemed to like me without saying much to me; and for once the subject of my English accent and whether it was illegal or not didn't come up. I was worried that we weren't paid a basic wage but would have to rely on tips. Nevertheless I turned up for work that Friday at nine o'clock after my other job and ready to work until two o'clock in the morning serving cocktails and drinks.

I noticed when I walked in that most of the gathering clientele were men. And a lot of them were alone as they sat around various tables surrounding the neon lit stage.

I went to the cloakroom and it was there that I discovered why.

It was basically a men's club for business men, and there was even a stripper. "I'm not going to bloody strip," I exclaimed to a nearby coloured girl, my English accent standing out more than ever.

"No, I am honey" she purred, "but I love your accent."

She told me that I was one of the waitresses and I would be waiting on tables like the other girls.

I relaxed then; that is until I saw what I'd have to wear. It was ten o'clock and the throbbing beat of "I Want your Sex" pulsated out from the two speakers behind the stage as the coloured girl writhed in time to the beat and slowly removed her clothes.

The faces of the men below glistened with sweat as their eyes never left her body as if they could somehow devour her and possess her just with their eyes.

I watched from behind a table in horror at the scene, something that I had heard about but had never witnessed.

And it sickened me. And it frightened me. Mike the manager bellowed at me, "Get from behind the fucking table." I moved out and moved amongst the men sitting at the tables. The black basque and black suspenders digging tightly into my body. The high heels throwing my body forward so I teetered as I walked.

I moved in and amongst them, taking their orders and bringing their drinks, avoiding their leering eyes and twisting away from their groping hands as I smiled a plastic smile and took their money.

I kept stuffing money into a glass at the bar and it was half past one when I felt vomit come up in my mouth, as the room became too hot for me to bear and I picked up the glass and went out the door back into the girl's cloakroom.

She was there. The black girl. She was standing naked in front of a long full length mirror and running her hands over her body and watching me staring at her intensely.

"Do you like what you see?" she said softly. "We can have some fun later, I've got some Coke." I reached for my clothes, emptied the glass and ran.

I took the lift down to the street and put my clothes on in it, leaving behind the outfit I'd worn, in a pile in the corner of the lift. I made my way out into the street, and away from there. The air felt fresh and cold and I pulled my coat around me and headed for 43rd Street. I stopped in the street, and pulled out the money and counted it. A lot of it was five or ten dollar bills, I couldn't believe it. I unwrinkled the money, and counted it up. Over a hundred dollars, I could put a deposit down, and save the rest gradually. It was one thirty in the morning but Manhattan never sleeps and I knew the little antique shop would still be open.

It was closed when I came to it, and the shutters bolted down. I pressed the bell again and again, until I could see someone moving inside from behind the shutters. The old man recognised me and he told me to wait while he lit the shop up and unlocked the door leaving on a thick security chain.
He told me straight away.
"You've come for the watch you wanted haven't you? Well you didn't put a deposit down did you, and I couldn't be sure you'd be back."
I couldn't believe it, "You've sold his watch."
The old man looked at me kindly. "I'm sorry I really am."

I walked off in the direction of the Port Authority, The money burning a hold in my pocket. If it wasn't going to be spent on the watch, it seemed like dirty tarts' money. How could I have done that. I wanted to get rid of it. Throw it away. It was easier than I thought.

I found a bar. And that night everyone was my friend. I drank drink after drink to drown the memory of the black girl's breasts and the men with their smell of sweat, and hungry eyes.

I didn't go home after that but stayed in the bar till the morning, then walked alone up to Nathans on Broadway and sat at a seat near the window and had something to eat.

I spent the rest of the day in the Library, flicking through Nietzsche and Kierkegaard and not making sense of any of it.
It was nearly seven o'clock when I headed towards 42nd street subway to get the train downtown and then the ferry back to the island.

I was walking quite slowly along Broadway, holding a can of beer in a brown paper bag to try to get rid of the memory of the night before and I heard distinctive voices and I noticed in front of me that it was them, 'The Children of Israel' again, the black racist group. They were shouting down their microphone more aggressively than ever and I noticed that James, or Lahab as he called himself wasn't there. So I joined the back of the crowd to listen to what they were saying.

The fat speaker, all dressed in white with a huge white cummerbund and a large white turban was shouting into the microphone, and to my horror as he saw me join the crowd he stopped his speech abruptly and stared at me so angrily that the whole crowd followed his eyes and turned to stare at me.

I was hungover and with no sleep all night I looked awful, like some old drunk clutching a can of beer.

"She's got a nerve to show her face," he boomed out, "a liar, coming here making fools of us filling us all up with lies over a newspaper."

I looked back at him, and opened my mouth to try and explain, but realised there was no point. There was no point to anything. And I went to move away; but just as I did, one of the brothers blocked my way. He'd been standing behind me watching the whole proceedings. He didn't have a turban like the others, just an off-white, thick, cable knit pullover, white trousers and a

243

distinctive medallion around his neck that contained a tiny red scorpion spider encrusted in a glass surrounding, and then edged in gold.

He held out a card with his phone number on it and told me that he was the 'Doctor'. He gave talks on herbs and herbal medicine, and the next one was in a few weeks and he wanted me to go. "If you phone me, I'll pick you up."

I looked at him intently. He was about sixty, grey hair shone out of the black woolly beard. But his face looked honest and sincere, and I smiled at him without it reaching my eyes, and stuffed the phone number into my bag and moved away.

"They" were back again. They seemed to be always present, as soon as darkness fell they would come out. They'd surround my bed in the dark and whisper at me.

Most of the time I couldn't make out what they were saying; it was too whispery or it would sound like they were saying it through a polythene bag so it was sort of huskily muffled. He still hadn't told me if he believed that it was possible to talk to the dead, and I kept on at him, until I received a reply.

Ian wrote again......

"The normal mundane consciousness of most of society is not our climate. Our climate is with the demons and angels. 'Demonfolk' I called M and I. I was shown the power they had that could be mine." (M - Myra Hyndley)

"Do you think that it is possible to be possessed by evil spirits? Sometimes I feel that I have all this evil inside me."

And again he answered me:

"It is not evil, I've told you before that it is energy. Before I met Myra it was all inside me, and the feeling of unreality kept me down. Like you, I feared it. The energy was kept in. When I met her she made me feel confident. She believed in me and looked up to me so much that I lost all fear, and the energy projected outwards and I lost control. To keep control, you must keep one eye on reality then you'll keep the edge.

I wrote back to him with an attempt at humour "You told me to keep one eye on reality; too late, it slipped away from me when I wasn't looking, and now none of it is real, and I feel compelled to write to you. But God, I feel that I don't have control anymore, the compulsions do, and they're coming from somewhere else. Where I do not know."

Another response....
"You say you feel compelled to do things. Always a compulsion and where does it come from? It comes from the higher self, the ego. The higher self impresses upon you, you cannot resist it. You are compelled to do its bidding. Compared to the mind, the higher self is incomparable in strength, one is a God, the other is a weak child. You just are compelled to do its will, then you try to philosophise and reason why you are doing the things that you do. And you try to work out a philosophy.

You say you feel guided to certain books that seem to rationalise what you are doing. I read De Sade, Nietzsche, Dostoevsky, through them I tried to reason with myself about what I was doing.

But I never could've stopped myself. I would sometimes wake in the morning and my higher self would not be there, the compelling self had vanished and it would just be me, and I would be like everyone else, and I would think that I was a madman, and I would get up and look at myself in the mirror and my eyes would look like someone else's, and it would return, like being possessed by evil spirits but it is not; it is, too much of yourself inside you."

I wrote:-
"But why did you kill, why were you compelled to do that? Why?"

He replied:
"They get you somehow, you see. But the reality was so unreal to me I had no real choice. They offered me the power to become a God, and I'm already in credit. You must learn that you too have the ability to become a God. You too are higher than they are, existing in a different realm.

The ones that are awake, are a totally different breed to the ones that are asleep. You and I are the same kind."

I awoke in a deep dread of fear and wondering why all around me seemed black, when it was morning. Then the dark haze before me thinned out slowly. I twisted round and out of bed and padded across the room to the huge mirror that I'd hung above the mantlepiece. The linoleum felt cold beneath my feet and I shivered slightly, the cold penetrating the thin material of the nylon nightdress that hung to just below my knee.

I'd just reached the mirror when I saw it staring back at me, not my face but an old man's; with glittering dark blackbird's eyes; I strained and strained to see myself but saw only him. And he wouldn't disappear; just stared back at me. An old man with a mocking face. Where had my face gone and had I turned into the old man? Who was the man, the one with the eyes like death who leered back at me from the mirror?

Ian wrote:-

"I think I believe that when you get so far, there are certain forces that want to stop you evolving. To keep us down. It turns people like us into killers. To stop us. To stop us growing , becoming to our full potential. So humanity can grow. It turns people like us into killers."

"How? How can it do that? . . . . .

"I don't know. People like us are vulnerable because we do not understand what is happening to us. We are in a world that we don't belong. We have nowhere to turn, we are weakened by this. And one day when you are not concentrating they will turn you into a killer or do what they did to me."

"What did they do to you?"

"I do not know."
"Why did they turn you into a killer? How did they do it?"

"I've told you, I do not know."

The telephone was ringing in the hallway, loud shrill rings and I ran downstairs to answer it. A deep black voice asked for me at the other end of it. It was the 'Doctor'. I'd phoned the number he'd given me earlier in the week and I'd left my number. He was holding one of his meetings on Sunday and did I want to go.

He offered to come and pick me up as he was out my way early in the morning, so I reeled off my address and arranged for him to collect me at about twelve.

Sunday came, and I enjoyed the ride from Staten Island over to Manhattan, the view from the bridge, and the novelty of being driven in a car, it seemed that I hadn't done that for ages. I got on well with him on the drive. He told me his name was Atari, and he'd been studying herbal medicine since his late twenties when his only son had died at only ten months old due to the administration of the wrong drugs by doctors. He didn't seem bitter at his baby's death but the strain of it had caused the end of his marriage and he'd been alone ever since.

I kept watching him on the journey. He had a kind face. His eyes had that look as if they'd seen everything and found it all painful. Above all he had that air of a kind of person that you could trust, and I remember I felt good that day; I felt that I'd made a friend. The first friend that I had made really, in Manhattan, apart from Lahab or James or whatever his name was.

The meeting that he took me to was in a small club type building on 54th Street. And the whole group consisted of two black men of about thirty, three black women, and Atari.

As soon as he sat down on a high stool in front of the group and started talking he captured my interest. He went through a kind of history of medicine, starting way back in the early days. He had a switch in his hand connected to a projector, and as he spoke kept flicking up slides on the screen.

I'd never really given much thought to medicine and how it'd come about. And I like a lot of people had an almost religious faith in my Doctor and hospitals. Atari's message was simple. "They had come a long way, but there was still a lot they didn't know, and mistakes were being made all the time. Doctors weren't to be seen as Gods and believed in, the way people did, and in a lot of areas it was a case of the blind leading the blind."

He finished off his talk by quoting from the Bible, the subtle messages about herbs, and how God had provided us with everything we needed for the cure of physical ailments in the natural medicines that he had given us. I sat as quietly as the rest of the group; then when the meeting ended, he asked me to stay behind, and we walked towards Port Authority together so I could catch the subway. I filled him in during the walk about how I'd soon have to move out of my room due to the fact that I didn't have a job (once again) and money was low, and he'd grabbed me by the arm and steered me into a nearby restaurant.

248

"I thought you looked ill, I bet you haven't eaten properly in weeks, you look like a skeleton."
I tried not to stuff the food down me too quickly when it arrived and kept pausing to talk to him, until he said "Talk later, eat now, and when you've had that, I'm going to fill you up with some of these puddings they have."

I grinned at him, and carried on eating. I had about 50 dollars left and no sign of a job, so I'd been only eating a bagel a day to try to save; and I was starving.

After we'd eaten, we talked some more, and he'd told me about the brothers, and how he'd met them, and how he'd felt lost before he met them.

I told him how I'd felt when I'd listened to Lahab speaking, and said how I agreed with what he'd been saying, about God and the spirit. I told him about my experience with the church and that I thought organised religion with its man made rules and hypocrisies made God seem judgmental and vindictive or weak and pappy. So many people who would've turned to God, didn't, because of the churches. He beamed at me, over the empty plates. "Do you know," he said excitedly "you would make a good wife for one of the brothers, they would make you very happy."

I stared at him as if he'd just jolted some sort of memory. "They would make you very happy." Someone else had said something similar to that. It was a while before it clicked of course. The psychic, Mike Baker! This J is the only man that can make you happy.

J.J. J for James. Lahab's real name? What else had the psychic said about him, oh yes, that he was self-employed.

I didn't want to come straight out with it, I would've sounded crazy. And doesn't every girl dream of a husband to love her and protect her forever, not just a man but more than a man, a hero.

I started tentatively. "Y'know that speaker, in the red robes, Lahab, is that his name, well I'm sure I saw him near 5th Avenue yesterday, does he work there?"

It worked. "No, he's self-employed, he's some sort of photographer."

I spooned another spoonful of ice cream into my mouth, I was nearly finished, so I let it slip slowly down my throat. Everything was magic again. It had slipped into that other state, and I felt bubbly and happy inside, like the whole world was a beautiful place where beautiful things happened or magic things: Unlike the normal way it was with me, all empty and dead.

So, soon, I wouldn't be alone. Soon, I'd be like one of the others; always happy; always smiling and belonging. How or when would it happen I asked myself, then decided that it was destiny and fate, so it'd happen anyway.

I linked arms with Atari as we came out of the restaurant and walked back towards Port Authority. I decided to tell him about Ian.

"Do you think it's wrong then? Do you think I should hate him, and are others right for hating him?."

"Hate what he has done, yes. But not hate him. He is not all powerful Lucifer. He is not evil. He is just a long way from God. So why hate, you must never hate anything, but if something is so far from God, as to not know the glory of God's love, then you must pity them or offer them help."

I beamed at him. I arranged to meet him again, then turned and waved as I ran down the steps to get the last train downtown. After that I saw him a great deal. Sometimes I'd meet him in the evenings about seven or eight o'clock and we'd to to the piano bars in the village.

I came to know nearly everybody in the bars and was introduced to the after dark black world and the clubs and bars where jazz musicians played, or where they specifically played New Orleans type music.

One of the clubs we went to, Atari introduced me to a singer there called Clyde. He had that funny Georgia accent and he'd join us for a drink and sit and laugh loudly with his black and white cotton wool head shaking in amusement, and there was his drawling deep voice. He'd always say he felt like singing love songs after talking to me, and he'd go back up stage and say 'this is for the pretty English lady' and he'd sing beautiful soul music for me.

Then, when it was over, he'd sometimes drive me home. And I'd sit in the car squashed between Atari and him, as we'd bumped and rattled all the way back to Staten Island in his battered old dusty Cadillac full of junk in the back seat.

Most of the time when I wasn't doing my temporary waitress jobs I'd pick up with those two, or I'd be in the huge library on 45th Street.

I'd found a section where you could pick out books from a huge reference section and place in your ticket and sit and read them. They had an amazing collection of really old books, and I was in my element in the occult section. I was trying desperately to find some sort of explanation to "them." Ian wouldn't say, apart from referring to them as "they" and assuming I knew what he meant. The thing is I did know what he meant but I just wanted to see if I could find out more about them.

It was one afternoon while I was in there skimming through the reference books, when I saw a book called 'The Maniac' written by Anonymous. I'd heard of the book ages ago in another about The Astral Plane, 'this

251

informative book' it'd called it. So I filled out a ticket and sat there to wait for it.

It was about half an hour before an old man with a trolley full of books drew up beside me and placed it in front of me.
It was a small red book with black writing on the front and no name where it normally has the name of the writer.

As I opened it I noticed that the pages were so thin and old that if I didn't turn them extra carefully, they kind of crumbled in my fingers. I turned back to the start of the book and noted the year it was published: 1901. Nearly a hundred years old. And I settled myself down to read it.

The story began with the writer introducing herself. She was a journalist who worked for a small newspaper and who lived alone; and the book was like an autobiography.

She'd had a normal existence up until one day while sitting at her desk, busy writing an article. She'd thought she had heard a voice, as if somehow talking to her inside her head. The woman opposite who told everybody she was some sort of psychic looked up sharply as it had spoken, then stared at her intensely.

She'd thought nothing more of it, until lying in bed one night, she'd heard them again, this time outside her head. "Listen to us, they had said, you have great psychic powers that will be destroyed if you ever divulge them to anyone else. We will encircle you and protect you from evil demons that want to possess you, but you must do as we say. She listened in horror at what they had told her, but thought to herself that she had better do as they say, as they probably knew more about demons and things than she did, and surely she must be special if they had chosen her to speak to.

252

It was a regular thing from then on that the voices would come to her at nights and say to her "If you do not run round the room five times, then empty all your clothes out of the wardrobe, you will be possessed by evil spirits."

Fearing the evil spirits she obeyed the voices and did what they told her. And it was nearly every night they came to her and she had to perform the rituals that they ordered to protect herself from demons. Gradually they started to interfere more and more in her life. They had a strange way of speaking in her head or sometimes she could hear them as purely her thoughts, but she knew they weren't her thoughts. They would tell her jokes on solemn occasions, so when she was interviewing somebody she would suddenly burst into hysterics of laughter over something "they" had said, in her head. They could come to her as she sat having dinner with friends and relatives and tell her to get up and out of her seat and run round the table twice then back to her seat or they would not be able to stop her being possessed by demons.

Eventually her sister began to notice her strange behaviour, her habits of running around the table for no reason and bursting out with laughter for no reason, and she forced her sister into being committed into an asylum against her will.

And so it came that she lost her job and her small flat and came to live in the asylum where she spent her days in bed, staring into space and listening to what they told her.
And it was one night as she lay in bed staring up into the darkness that she all of a sudden heard deep low cruel sniggering. The laughing went on for such a long time that she sat up in bed and said, "What is it, why are you laughing?"

"Do you know what they call us?" the voice said, followed by more mocking laughter.

"No" she half whispered.

"The invisible liars. And do you know what we call you? Land of Idiots. Cohort of fools. Blinded by your world of illusions."

It was a week later when she found herself seated in front of her psychiatrist fully dressed and ready to be discharged.

"So you've experienced insanity, and made a miraculous recovery. Obviously our treatments worked, I am extremely pleased," said her psychiatrist.

After a while she took up another appointment as a journalist on a different newspaper and it was then that "they" started to come back to her.

She'd ignore them at first but they became more and more of a nuisance, sometimes even her writings were not her own.

It was on the advice of an old workmate who she bumped into on the street that she sought help. The woman, who called herself a psychic asked her out of the blue whether she still had trouble with them, then she'd slipped her a card with a phone number on it and the name of what seemed to be some sort of Doctor.

"Eat red meat, drink plenty of wine and get yourself a husband and sleep with him regularly, the strange old man had told her when she'd made an appointment to see him. "If you do all that, then I'll help to keep you earthbound in the same way I eat little and drink only water so I can study them. I'm what's known as an occultist. You are extremely lucky, and if you wish to progress, then you must take up study or you will be lost in a world you don't understand. If they come again, ignore them. If they are ignored then it isn't much sport to them, and they'll look elsewhere."

She sat for a while with the occultist and he explained more about what had happened to her. "Unfortunately," he went on, "there is a web, that separates the spirit from the physical in some people. The web is damaged, or, in others, they are sometimes pushed back through it in a painful childhood, when the web is weak. It means that these people are a different type. They see it all differently, they experience phenomena that is outside the normal experience of others.

It is what the ones that know only of the physical call 'madness'. But all it is, is a different consciousness. The spirit consciousness or higher consciousness.

These people are victim to many things in that world. It is the world of thought and the world of emotion. They experience over-strong emotions and thought interference. And where do they go for help? A psychiatrist.

If an occultist could gain access to the inmates of the asylums then, they would be no more than half full than they are normally." "Why half?" she asked curiously.
"Oh, some are lost for good you see. Lost in a world they don't understand, they drift away, their minds destroyed by thoughts and ideas that drive them into that state or a state of destruction, to others or to themselves."
"The invisible liars," she interrupted.
"Oh, yes they do much damage. It's sport to them you see, and they know their world well. It is theirs, so they play many advanced tricks and illusions to entrap a vulnerable one, like a wicked man could play many a cruel trick on a blind child on our plane, so are we to them."

I finished the book and closed it. My head ached. I'd been sitting in the Library and reading solidly for over five hours.

I handed in the book back and walked down towards Nathans and sat at the table where I always sat, near the window, and drunk some of the coffee I'd ordered, slowly, deliberately, the answers were there. My whole life, there before me, explained. And Ian? All that he had written became clear and meaningful.

I sat there thinking over what I'd read for what seemed like ages, then walked along towards the occult shop along 53rd Street.

I began browsing the shelves for a while, I'd read most of the books ages ago and none of them had told me anything. I was browsing with a frown on my face, when the youngish man behind the till noticed me and asked me if there was anything particular that I wanted.

I thought back to the book I'd just read, "Yes, I want something an occultist might study." I went to explain further but I noticed that he'd grabbed a pencil and was jotting something down on a piece of paper. He handed it to me and I read it over 'The Theosophical Bookshop, 54th Street'.
"Whats that 'Theosophical'?"

He explained to me, that that was what I wanted 'Theosophy' and that they only really handled basic stuff there.

The shop I came to on 54th Street, The Quest Bookshop, was kind of like a university bookshop full of what seemed like text books. I let instinct guide me, and spent all the spare money I had.

After that I was a regular there and I stuck to two main writers, Charles Leadbetter and A.E. Powell and I read anything that I could get my hands on that they had written.

I felt that I was learning, and I filled my letters to Ian about what I was

256

learning.

He wasn't impressed. *"I've read all there is on the occult, Satanism, Aleistair Crowley. It's all childish credulous rubbish."*

I kept on at him. "I know all that, that stuff just gives it all a bad name, but this is different. You'll understand it. You will, honest. It explains why you did it. It wasn't you, or 'M', but them. Pulling you, pushing you, making you do it. You weren't in control, they were.

He still wouldn't have it. "Read Neitzsche or Schopenhauer for the real answers."

I think it was while I was writing a letter to him that it suddenly clicked. I felt that I'd been learning from him, learning all about the feelings of unreality, the voices, the differences between us and other people.

And yet, I refused to listen to Nietzsche because he'd gone insane, lost himself somehow. Yet what about Ian? In an asylum for the murder of children, so many children, killed so viciously and all in the manner of a man carrying out a mission. Making lists and keeping sequences as if it all had some deep purpose. *'I did them favours, I'm in credit now'*, he had written. As if there had been some purpose. A great big reason for all he had done.

I flicked through my books. Surely, there must be some reference to this sort of thing. Surely. It didn't take me long to find it.

"Woe to those who let themselves
be used by the stronger forces
As instruments of the veil they
become as guilty as the force
they are used by."

It couldn't be true, I looked again through other books.

"Evil and depraved entities
find vulnerable minds that they
can drive to the basest of depravation
and ultimate evil acts, then
they revel in their commission."

So it was possible. I read more.

"The time span is limited."

I remembered what he had said, *'I felt that time was running out. Things kept coming into my mind and seemed exciting, they weren't when I carried them out, and I got more and more outrageous until I got sucked into a death dive and lost control, I lost sight of reality'.*

Lost. Lost.

I felt as if I knew something that he didn't. But for all that time I'd thought that God would somehow save him, or he'd be forgiven. Was everyone right and I wrong?

His life was so awful now, would it continue after death?

I thought of some of his letters to me, the warmth of someone who really cared about another person. The loneliness of someone who wanted a family, and someone to care for him and to care about.

Would, on judgement day, that warmth be crushed and destroyed? And lost from God forever? That was what hell was, endless separation from love and warmth. But what of him on judgement day?!!

258

If he was pure evil then he wouldn't need the warmth, he'd revel in the cold. And I knew all about his vulnerability 'Why did you do it? Why didn't you kill yourself to stop yourself? Did you get <u>that</u> lost? Do you still believe them? Still I believe that you are invincible? That they will come through at the end of the day? And if you think that, then you can't turn to God, because you'll be turning your back on them.

Them. Them. Don't you know what they call them?

I felt hot and sick inside. When my mind grasped some sort of answer, it seemed somehow too slow and heavy to lock into it. And I felt lost again, and realised I knew nothing. I was like a blind man, feeling and groping my way and thinking that I was getting somewhere, only to realise that I had thought myself into a sort of cul-de-sac.

I wanted to confide in someone. Someone who would understand. Someone who wasn't as lost in it all as I was, and Ian was. The 'Doctor' seemed to be the obvious choice.

I'd been seeing him for quite a long time by then. Old Atari; not as a boyfriend, but we were good friends. And the only friend I had made really, in the whole time I'd been in Manhattan.

I'd confided in him around then, and he'd told me that he understood, and not to worry, just to put my faith in God.
And I couldn't believe it. Ian had told me to keep myself to myself, it was dangerous to be open about things like that. *'Tell no-one, I'm telling you that for your own good'. They'll think you're an idiot or disturbed if you start confiding in them; It's not a reality for them.'*

He'd been wrong. It was alright to trust people and the 'Doctor' proved it by accepting me, even after I'd told him about 'them'.

I started having the flu type colds again, like I'd had last winter. I think really that it was a combination of not eating properly and the fact that I couldn't get used to the freezing New York temperatures. It was another Sunday when Atari had one of his meetings and I made my own way this time, across on the ferry and uptown on the subway.

I remember that day and I remember that I felt a bad feeling in my stomach and I felt miserable and had to practically drag myself there. But I figured it was due to the cold that had turned into a head cold and I was feeling muzzy and weak and achey like you do the day before you go down with flu. I'd got to the meeting and I noticed that there was quite a few faces I didn't know.

I went to hug Atari and was surprised when he moved away, and cast a glance over to the people sitting around in a circle, waiting to begin. I was the only white face there but that wasn't too unusual. And I noticed a lot of black girls of about my age that glared at me when I sat down. And a few men that had come from the Children of Israel school, where their philosophies were taught.

The meeting got under way, and I sat there feeling more and more woozy, the overheated small room started getting stuffier and stuffier and I was feeling worse. My throat had seized up and it hurt when I swallowed, and I kept sniffing because I couldn't find a tissue.

"Don't sniff, use a goddamn napkin," the 'Doctor' half spat at me. I looked up at him surprised and the black girls opposite sniggered loudly.

I remember I sat there and got the feeling that something was wrong, and I started to feel that horrible feeling of fear that sometimes rises up inside when you're in a bad situation.

My head felt so slow and achey I stopped listening to the lecture the

260

'Doctor' was giving and just sat there. Then, tuned in again a while later to hear that he was talking about Racism. And he seemed to have got everyone in the room wound up to a sort of anger as he reeled off various injustices committed against black people by the whites of America. I glanced up at the black girls opposite me and noticed that they were glaring at me with intense hatred. And I swallowed hard, feeling the sore lump in my throat. I felt awful and I wanted to go, I couldn't take this.

I was looking at the 'Doctor' and wishing he'd stop but he kept on going, then turned his gaze to me.

I saw my chance "I'm not a racist, I think it's bad too," I started weakly. He was ignoring me. "Y'see folks, here's this white girl and she wants to be black. That's why she's here. She knows black is superior." I didn't mind what he was saying. It was no worse than what a lot of white people said about black people

But he was continuing and I couldn't quite believe what I was hearing. Hadn't he understood? Accepted me and understood?
He was going on and they were all staring at me with looks somewhere between contempt and amusement. And the small room seemed to get smaller than it was, smaller and hotter.

Just the 'Doctor's' voice droning on, mocking in derision. "This white girl is like all her kind. Their minds are weak. She's involved in, hell, loads of trouble," he raised his hands in the air, "mixed up with an evil man who slaughtered children. She's in a hell of a lot of trouble in her country. That's why she came here. And when she did, she realised that it was black people that had God. She believed in what Lahab was saying. She knew she was evil."

My mind went back to the first time I had seen The Children of Israel, the

261

speaker in the red robes and his philosophies of spirit. Did I think that? Did I think that I was evil? The room spun and I was about to cry. I felt ill and confused and too hot. I could see the black girl's faces opposite me smiling cruelly. And the air filled with hatred.

He was still talking, "Do you know this white girl is so weak in the head like all her kind, she thinks that she can talk to spirits?"

I could hear raised levels of laughter. And hot tears filled my eyes and I bowed my head and allowed them to slide down my face, unashamedly.

"And being white she doesn't think she's crazy. She asks this man who was so crazy out of his evil white mind he killed small children, whether she is mad or not. How's that for the way white minds think."

I felt as if I'd been made to undress in front of them and now they were twisting me round and finding faults with my naked body. He turned to me - "What did you tell me you thought of the white people here in New York?"

I looked up at him "Too rich" and I faltered - "greedy. I think I told you I thought that they were greedy."
"And the black people?"
"Well, when I saw James, I mean Lahab, I thought that he was the nearest thing to goodness I'd ever seen. I turned back to God because of him, before I was lost."
"And what do you think he thinks of you?" he shouted.

I heard a girl's laugh and I raised my head and looked at the 'Doctor's' eyes, full of venom. "He thinks you're nothing but a crazy mixed-up white lady, that told him a lot of lies and made him feel a fool. He can't stand you. He said you made a nuisance of yourself, kept phoning him, and

saying you had to meet him."
Those things; would someone that I was going to marry say such things?
The 'Doctor' was still talking. "And his wife's just given birth to a
beautiful baby boy."

The tears came heavier, and I hated myself.

"And this girl with her pale face somehow thinks she's in with a chance."

I went numb. How had he known that? Oh, I supposed it was obvious I'd
spoken about him enough. He'd probably just guessed. After all I'd
confided in him about virtually everything in my life.

And now I sat there, all my secrets, all my special secrets exposed. All the
magic, and all the hopes, lay stamped on and revealed, not as the treasures I
thought them, but stupid crazy dreams. The dreams and hopes of a girl who
was out of her mind. A crazy white girl. My mind full of stupid empty
thoughts of Psychics. - J. Soulmates. - Voices. - Ian Brady. As if anyone
would want to marry someone like me. Least of all the man who I had
thought so beautiful, whose wife that he loved and who had just given him
a son. Just the dreams of a crazy white girl.

He was right. All that he said was right. And I got up and went and stood in
the Hallway, then saw an empty dark room and stood in it and sobbed
endlessly.

I remembered the white people stepping out of the limousines in their long
fur coats, dripping in their diamonds along Broadway, off to see the latest
show. Stepping over the bodies of the black beggars in the street open to
the cold.

I remembered the young black boy who stood at Times Square subway who talked of God and valued a smile over a few cents. Was he right? Was he right? I was standing in the room, in the dark and sobbing.

I felt arms move around me and I turned in fright, it was Atari. "Look, I've arranged with one of the sisters in there for you to go and share her flat with her."

"But they hate me" I interrupted.

"There y'see, that's your paranoia. You're crazy, you know you are, and the first thing I'm going to do is to see you stop writing to that man, the one that killed those children. He's evil and he's an evil influence on you, telling you these crazy things'.

I looked up at him. "Do you think he is evil?"

"Didn't you tell me you'd lost all your friends over him,because they know he's evil?"

I nodded.

"You're going to go even crazier if you continue to write to that madman. I'll sort your head out, before you get in any more trouble and have to leave this country. I'll look after you from now on, and I'll oversee everything you do. You can't take care of yourself, do you understand? You need me. You can't cope on your own."

I nodded, and wiped the tears away with the back of my hand.

He told me he'd pick me up tomorrow and take me to the girl's flat, where he'd take care of me.

I nodded again, and he walked me to the elevator. The doors were closing and he told me he'd see me at twelve the following day. "I really do care about you, you know," I heard him say, and the lift moved and the doors opened out onto the street.

I got the train straight down to South Ferry. And I started crying again. I got to the Ferry terminal and I decided to try and phone someone to help me. I phoned the dial code for London, then The Sunday People number to try to speak to Phil. I was told that he was out by the newsdesk, but a girl took my number to get him to call me back later.

I put the phone down then dialled another number from memory. 'Louise' a friend from school.

She gasped as she heard my voice "Everyone thought you were really sick" she intoned, voice full of contempt.

I slammed the phone down before she could continue. I'd forgotten the newspaper stuff. I couldn't face all that again.

I dialled again, the last number I could think of, David my old boyfriend. He answered in the familiar friendly voice then when I told him it was me he went silent.

"What's up?" I gasped, beginning to cry again in fear. What else. "What is it."

"Last Sunday, more stuff about you in the papers. They said you're his girlfriend and that you're amazed that he can two time you from in there, Park Lane. And you're going to pull her apart limb from limb."
"What?"
"Oh come on, you said it, don't play the innocent."
"Said what? No I didn't; what other girl? There aren't any girls, and I'm not his girlfriend. The Sunday People won't be pleased when they see that."
"It's The Sunday People it was in," he half shouted, "Hang on, I've got it here, Phil Hall, written by Phil Hall."
I went silent.
"Didn't you know?"

"No he made it up. He knows I'm in America so he knows he'd get away
with it, oh and even if I wasn't, what am I going to do about it?.". . . Phil
Hall has a copy of a letter from Ian Brady stating that I'm his daughter, so
how come he's written that story."
In my anger I'd forgotten what I'd called him for, then it came back to me,
but he was speaking before I could say anything.

"Anyway, who cares, you're mad, everyone knows that. You always have
been. Everyone always used to say it about you, my Mum and the others."

I went quiet. "Am I? Am I really mad?"
"Yeah, you are. Get help. You need help."
"David, do you, do you think it might be true that we're evil and away from
God, and black people are close to God?"
He snorted in derision "You're a joke, y'know that."

He hung up. I replaced the receiver and stood there leaning up against the
call box. I could barely think for confusion.

Thank God and the 'Doctor'. I'd be o.k. if I stuck with him. He'd look after
me. Make sure nothing bad happened to me. I couldn't cope with all this. I
didn't know what to do and I was doing everything wrong.

I took the ferry across to Staten Island, and then the bus home. The first thing
I noticed when I got in the door was one of his letters, it was in the kitchen.
Long blue air mail envelope with his sloppy handwriting. I reached to open
it, then thought again and ripped it into tiny, tiny shreds that made retrieving
it impossible and let it flutter down into the wastebin in the kitchen.

The phone started to ring and I rushed to pick it up. It was Phil Hall.

I screamed my anger about the story he'd written. I needed to talk to him. I needed a friend.

"Phil listen, they keep saying I'm mad, tell me I'm not, please tell me, it's frightening me."
"You thought you were Ian Brady's daughter for godsake and you're telling me you're not mad."

I started to get hysterical.
"He is all I have Phil. In the kid's home, that's all I had. And that was what I was told. I didn't make it up. How can that mean I am mad?"

He didn't answer. All he said was, coldly, "You should have coped better. Others like you do."
I held the phone pressed to my ear. I had slept with this man. Been so physically close. Yet someone with whom I had nothing in common.

"You can't keep ringing me, what is it you want from me? I feel that I have to be nice to you and call you back in case you tell people about what happened in France, the romance we had; me stupidly thinking that I was in love with you."

I let the phone slip slightly. "You don't have to be nice to me, nothing happened, you were just drunk, I'm not going to tell anyone" I said mechanically, my eyes glazing as if everything had slipped into a dream."
"Look", he went on "I know that where you're living is a prostitute area, that happens to a lot of girls who grow up in orphanages and children's homes. You're desperate for money but I don't want any trouble, I've just applied to the News of the World for a job. If anyone knows I saw you or was interested in someone like you, it could be bad for me."

"I'm not desperate for money, I've got a job."
I started to cry as the realisation of what he'd said to me sunk in. "I'm not a

prostitute, I'd never be. Ian wouldn't let me for starters. I have got family. I'd lose him if I stooped to that level." I started sobbing, "Why are you saying this?"

"I don't want someone like you phoning me and causing trouble just because we made love. It meant nothing. Tell me how much you want and I'll send it to you. But cut this crap out with the phone calls. It's embarrassing."

"But you told me to keep in contact" I whispered. "It was you that asked me."

"That was when I thought it was a story. There's no story between you and Brady now. An insider at the hospital says it's a big joke there. Brady thought he had this daughter and someone who didn't think he was worthless. And then she writes to him and starts to tell him she hears voices. His great friend he's been boasting about turns out to be some sort of nut. A crank. They're all laughing at him."

I let the phone swing, and then it fell to the floor.

Tomorrow would be here soon. And then everything would be alright. He'd look after me. Sort everything out. Take care of me, and stop all the pain.

I slept fitfully that night and tossed and turned and heard 'them' again telling me to wake up, wake up. Then I was dreaming again and I dreamt that I was locked up in a room. The Doctor was there. And he kept the key.

The next scene and he was lying naked on top of me, pushing himself inside me. And I was lying there, motionless. I was seeing myself as if from a distance and I appeared to have no life in myself. I looked pale. Disconnected. Dark circles surrounded my eyes. Displaced. Not there. I did what he wanted me to do. He was who I was dependent on. I needed him I couldn't cope without him. I was mad. It was either him or the confines of an institution. And yet I was institutionalized with him. Dependent on him, even to tell me when to eat. I was not free.

And I lived in a kind of perpetual fear. A fear of life. A fear of living. A fear of being myself. A crazy girl out of control.

And I awoke the next morning, late. But I felt that I was awake for the first time in a long while. I felt that the girl who was strange and crazy was there and I didn't care any more. She got me into all the trouble. But at least she was strong.

I dressed quickly and packed my suitcase even quicker. It was eleven o'clock. The 'Doctor' would be here in an hour, maybe he'd come early. I flicked quickly through an old newspaper I had lying around. Flights to London 110 dollars, I used the phone in the hallway.

I just had time to scrawl out a letter and stuff it into an envelope.

"Ian,
I know what they're saying about me. Why the hell are you still writing to me when they're all saying I'm crazy and laughing at you? Why didn't you tell me?
Don't let anyone split us up. You know the way families carry on. They keep on loving each other through everything. We're ;like that. o.k.?
Let's make a promise here and now. To never let each other down and not stick up for each other.
You're all I've got in the world.
You see with each other we'll cope. And everything will be o.k. Everything will always be alright for us if we stay together and look out for each other, like they do.
Let's swear it now. For keeps. For always.

It was ten to twelve by the time I ran down the steps of the old house to the bus stop at the end of the garden. And it was only when I was sitting at the back of the bus five minutes later that I turned and looked back to it. 1936

Richmond Terrace. It had always seemed so sad and so old.

It was strange to think that I'd never sit in that attic room again.

I felt sad somehow, it was the only home I'd had really, apart from when I lived with my long time foster family.

The ferry docked at South Ferry and I got the train uptown to 30th Street and waited for the bus to the airport to catch the flight to London at 3.00.

The bus came, and the driver gave me a hand heaving my suitcase into the side of the bus.
"Going far?" he asked.
"London."
"Oh that far" he laughed "didn't you like it in New York?"

Not many people boarded the bus and eventually it started up and it drove up through Broadway and Times Square. My mind filled with memories of the afternoon when I'd come there and gaped out the cab window as I saw my first sight of the tall buildings and all that bustle of Broadway. I'd thought that it'd be alright then. I'd thought that that was it. Where I belonged. And when I'd heard that speaker. Everything had been full of magic, and hope.

But now all hope had gone. And no dreams were left. The bus moved slowly and passed the sex shops near 42nd Street and the black people begging and standing around the burning brassieres just like they did on the Rocky films.

As soon as the plane landed in England I felt a kind of blind panic inside me. I didn't know what I was doing back there, and I felt scared. I felt as though something awful was about to take place.

I slept on the plane and I had this dream. I was like everyone else, a woman who lived in this house, like a home, and I was married to this man that I loved so much, and in the dream there were two beautiful children that I adored who were mine and loved me in return. In the dream I felt so safe, so secure. My husband loved me, adored me, there was no pain anymore and I couldn't believe my luck. I had someone; no more lonely Christmasses and birthdays. I was like everyone else, all warm and secure in this house, this home. And it was one day I'd gone out to the shops, I only took a short while, then when I came back, the door was locked and I couldn't get in. And I thought, strange, and I knocked and this woman answered.

And I looked at her and said "Who are you?" and she looked at me and said "Who are you dear?" And I said "But I live here." And she laughed. Then I heard my husband coming and I thought thank God, he would sort it out. And he came to the door. My husband, my darling, my baby, and he put his arm round this woman and he called her 'darling'.
"What is it darling?" he said to her.
"Who is this woman? What is it she wants?"
And then my children appeared at her side and they clung to her, and they asked the woman
"Who is she, why doesn't she go away?"
And I looked at my husband and I said "But I'm yours. You love me."
And he laughed and looked at his wife and said "Honestly darling would I love someone like her?"
And they looked at each other with so much love and devotion. Then they turned their back on me and they went back inside their house. Together. There was no-one again that was the other half of me.

271

And as I walked away I could hear their laughter echo around my head. And I kept walking and I could see myself reflected in a shop window. Blonde hair, dyed, black roots, tarty make-up and stupid ugly face and I looked and I realised that I was a fool to think of him as mine, to think that he could've loved me back.

And I was just the crazy woman who lived on the corner who stares out of the window all the time. Lonely and mad, and living in her dreams.

I'd seen the home, and the family within and I'd been so mad that I'd believed that I lived there too. But it was just a dream, not real, and I <u>was</u> mad. Mad and alone, and standing in the street. Outside all the other houses, with the warmth of the lights on in the windows. Outside looking in and just a joke.

I woke as the plane landed, and then felt that awful feeling. The panic.

I stood by the telephone kiosk in the arrival lounge wondering what to do. Who to phone. In the end I came up with Ted Hynds. He picked me up two hours later outside Terminal 3. Then told me I could stay for 2 or 3 nights, no more.

He lived in a flat overlooking Kew Green and it was quite beautiful really, all full of antique stuff but it had loads of paperwork all over the floor of his front room, unfinished newspaper stories.

I told him the story of what happened to me in New York leaving out all the stuff about Ian and the 'Doctor', and he kept laughing and turning it all into a joke. I felt good then, I felt glad I'd come back, and I relaxed a bit for the first time in ages.

"Look, our newspaper uses your old firm Rinaldis for our detective work now. If you like I'll see if they'll have you back."

He went quiet and realised what he'd said. I could tell that he was thinking of Alan and the dirty trick he'd played on me that started all the media interest in me.
"I've known about Alan for ages, I'm not that stupid. I'd always assumed he asked for money though."
"He's a very clever man, no-one's fool", said Ted sternly.

Ted fell silent and so did I. I hadn't wanted to go back to Rinaldis anyway. There were other agencies, I'd just get one, the other side of London, where they knew nothing about me.

Of course we'd drink a lot and I ended up staying there the week sleeping in his bed while he used the settee. And I'd meet him from work and sit in "The Stag" pub with all his cronies and listen to them all talking shop. One night, Frank Thorn, the Daily Mirror reporter was teasing us about our relationship. I was pleased when Ted made it clear, that he thought of me as his 'niece' and there was no intimacy between us.

Ted had gone on about Ian's letters so much that I showed him some that I had. Anyway those with anything private in, I'd destroyed.

Ted didn't seem to think that they had 'Nothing in them' and he was particularly interested in one where Ian had said he believed Myra's sister had been carrying his child at the time of the trial *'I've tried to get a good look at him but haven't managed to'* - Ted wanted it.

And he didn't like the snippets of what he read in the rest of the few letters I'd shown him.
"These are shocking."
They're not shocking."
"They frighten me so they must've frightened you."
Ted gave me back the letters. But not all of them!

273

The next Sunday in The Sunday Mirror where he'd thought I'd not look "MYRA'S SISTER HAD MY BABY" the headline screamed and a reference to a series of shocking letters and a so-called quote by me that I was terrified and sickened by the letters.

I'd moved out of Ted's by then, and got a job as a live-in receptionist in a hotel until I found my feet. And when I read it, I was livid. A letter from Ian arrived three days later. "I've just read the article in the Sunday Mirror. *Did anything I say frighten you? I never meant to terrify you. It hurts me badly to think that I sickened you.*"

I didn't answer it, just took it down to the Mirror Group Building and demanded to see Ted.

He was in his 'Uncle Ted' character when I finally did get to see him.

"I want you to stop writing to him", he pleaded.
"It's none of your bloody business."
"Those letters frightened me, what I saw of them."
"So what, they weren't even the private ones, I destroyed them."
"I hate to imagine what they said. Look Christine, it's not a normal thing for a twenty three year old to be doing, and some of those things I read frighten me, so God knows what they did to you"
I sighed loudly "You don't understand."
"No, it is you that doesn't understand."

He dragged me into the lift and up to the Library section where they kept all the newspaper clippings. And I stood there wondering what he was doing.

He began talking to the girl behind the desk, then a few moments later she came from behind a shelf with a whole pile of newspaper clippings and gave them to Ted.

Ted flicked through them, then handed them to me.

Clippet after clippet of girlfriend stories. Women writing to Ian Brady to tell them that they loved him. The room started to drift away and I could feel a film of sweat forming on my upper lip.

"This is a joke." I half whispered.
"Come on, you're worth more than these slags."
I looked at him and felt everything swim, "Maybe I am one of these slags."
He laughed "Come on, you don't love him. These women write and tell him that they love him, and they can't live without him."

I looked down at the clippets. Photograph after photograph. One after the other. "I am Brady's Sex Slave" screamed one headline, and a girl, 34 "I often visit where he lived for my holidays and when my boyfriend sleeps with me, I cry out Ian, Ian. I carry his letters everywhere and...."

I stopped reading and handed them back to Ted.
We went down in the lift together and I stood behind him and watched the back of his head. I was in a dream, and like in a dream I might at any moment take my clothes off or piss in the street, like you do in a dream. I was out of control. But I'd cope.

But now the solid ground had slipped from underneath me and everything was fuzzy and unreal. Ted led me around the corner to the pub and I floated after him. We sat in 'The Stag' and Ted bought me a glass of wine and other journalists joined us and Ted introduced me.

A lot of them remembered me from the story 'I AM BRADY'S DAUGHTER' and they looked at me curiously.

"I've been showing Christine those stories, all those women writing to Ian

Brady declaring their undying love, telling him how they can't live without him."

The group started to laugh and talk about them amongst themselves. And I sat there listening.
"One of them is quite pretty, so I heard, and she's really mad about him."
I could feel something inside me, some sort of anger that was twisting around, and trembling to come out, but I couldn't put my finger on what it was.

I looked up, and squeezed on the glass I had in my hand, "He writes to a lot of people, he told me so, they don't visit him though, he only writes to be polite.

A woman journalist was speaking now "No," she said surprised, "this young thing goes up to see him all the time. He's quite taken with her, too."

I saw her pretty face in my mind. She did look pretty. Beautiful really. Like an angel. Prettier than I could have ever looked. And sweet too. Sweet and pure like nice girls are.

The pub had got more crowded and the juke box was playing loudly. I looked at Ted and he was staring at me intensely.

He leant forward, and his closeness made me feel shut in, claustrophobic "You see," he whispered "you're nothing to him. I doubt if he'd even miss you if you stopped writing. He wouldn't even notice."
I wanted to grab hold of his arm and tell him everything. But he was standing up and he was going. But tell him what, anyway?
Most of the crowd had thinned out and I was left with Mydrim Jones, a short, Welsh, Sunday People journalist I'd seen many times before.
"I'll stand you dinner if you're hungry ."

I looked up at him. I didn't want to be alone so I nodded and downed the rest of the drink in front of me and followed him out of the pub.

I remember we ended up somewhere in Covent Garden. And we sat opposite each other and he was making small talk in that distinctive Welsh accent.

But I wanted to talk about them, the newspaper clippings Ted had shown me. He knew all about them and he went on a tirade of abuse about loopy women and crime groupies and finished off with a sneer.

He looked at me, and I was crying.

He put down the menu "You don't mind if I change my mind about buying you dinner do you? I can't believe Ted didn't know about you. You're just one of these stupid tarts who're obsessed by him. Worthless little slags like you are ten a penny."

I thought that he'd stop, but he carried on "What's the attraction, like it rough? Like the idea of a bit of blood, him dominating you? Being some sort of slave? I'll get you that tape he made, then you won't be so turned on, or would that excite you even more?....

He was going on and I wasn't listening. I was just aware of the knife running back and forth over my thumb and the way it hurt; hurt so much it made me concentrate on it and the blood that was making a mess on the tablecloth.

He dropped me off at the tube station and drove off.

I turned and saw myself reflected in a darkened shop window, blonde hair dyed and tarty dark roots, high heels, cheap skirt, cheap blouse and ugly face.

There was an off-licence and it was open and I bought a bottle of wine and got the man in the shop to uncork it. Then I drank it like a wino on the tube, with all the office workers coming home from their nine to five.

They kept looking at me in disgust; the girl who sat there sobbing hysterically, with the mascara streaked down her face and onto her blouse and the bottle of wine on her knee from which she kept swigging.

But what did it matter? What did anything matter?

I got back to my room. Back to my stinking little bedsit, that smelled of rotting cabbage. Where I lived alone by myself.

Alone with my madness.

There was a letter on the bed, I'd been starting to write to him to reply to his letter. It was all about voices in the head and justifying it. Followed by telling him how much I cared about him. Needed him.

I threw up in the small sink in the corner of my room over the slot meters. Then raised my head and looked at myself in the mirror.

Then dug tiny scratches with my nails into the face of the girl that I hated.

THE EDITOR'S EPILOGUE

While it is recognized that this book is the story of the life of Christine Hart, it is by way of association with Ian Brady that necessitates its publication. When I read it for this purpose, I realized that the readers deserved to know what Brady had written about his thoughts and ideas and what, if anything other than just pure unadulterated evil, promulgated his actions. The book contains, perhaps, the first account that he has issued of those dark days of crime and murder. We have left out his association with Myra Hindley having satisfied ourselves that Emlyn Williams in his work, 'Beyond Belief' said all that there was to say on that matter.

It is both Brady's and Christine's comments and revelations about inner 'voices' that dominated their every move, and it is that which intrigues me . . . .

I know a man called Bob. More to the point I know his parents and have done so for more than thirty years. Bob comes from a good home. A middle class reasonably well off background. He has a happily married brother and parents that have been together as a couple forever. Bob attended junior school and with the results of his term's work impressed his teachers to a point whereby they were totally confident of his ability to pass sufficient of his eleven plus exams to qualify for grammar school. He failed them miserably. His headmaster suggested that the pressure of exams may have been the problem and that he ought to attend a small secondary school where the classes were not of such size so as to cause him unnecessary stress. His parents found an exclusive public school for boys, and he later gained seven passes in his G.C.E. exams, going on to college and university where he earned himself a B.A. Degree. Not, you would say, a subject for becoming a vehicle for the 'voices'.

How different his background to that of Ian's and Christine's; does it defy the theory that only a deprived, loveless, and unhappy childhood is the only environment for a human being to become basically what the medical profession call a schizophrenic.

Bob is now thirty, and for the last ten years he has been a depressive whose life is totally dominated and guided by the 'voices'. Fortunately, in Bob's case the 'voices' are not instructing him to kill. In fact quite the reverse. Bob has recently left the apartment he shared with his beautiful young lady to live alone in what can only be described as a hovel; a house inhabited by drunks and down and outs. He still visits Gillian, but he dare not sleep in the apartment overnight for fear that the attackers who threaten to murder him with eye slashing stilettos, also attack her. That, he calmly states, as if it were about to happen at any moment, is his sole reason for not living with her anymore, and also the reason why the police found him lying in a field close to death waiting for these aliens to kill him. So real are his 'voices' that he nearly died waiting for the confrontation, oblivious to the needs of food and drink, warmth and comfort. Bob also tried to end his life, and cannot work because of this. He needs regular injections of Flupenthixol (Depixol) and daily doses of Procyclidine to avoid the side effects. This will not cure his fixations but will help him cope with them . . .

The word schizophrenic usually suggests to the layman, a dual personality . . . Doctor Jekyll and Mr. Hyde. I believe that the medical profession uses the term to indiscriminately describe those people who suffer from the 'voices' . . .

So what of Christine and Ian Brady? I must make it clear that as a father and indeed a grandfather, I cannot feel sympathy for the man, and my heart continuously goes out to the families and most of all to the parents of those children that Brady murdered. Every time they hear a jingle, watch afternoon television, see or hear a child laugh, or cry, their hearts must sink into their feet. Sympathy however, or the lack of it, must not be confused with understanding. For it is the knowledge of what was behind Brady's actions that may help the psychiatrists and psychologists to understand, and to progress and, one day, even to cure. Or, are the 'voices' real? Many think that they are uncurable because they originate from a spirit world. A time and place, a plane different from our own. If Brady was a victim, an exceptionally receptive vehicle, then was he totally in control of the dreadful things that he did? I remember well the weeks that followed his arrest and the trial. The whole Nation was in a state of confusing depression . . . .

And Christine? Only a blood test or a DNA test will prove conclusively that Ian is her father. There were probably a number of Marys living in Hull at about the time he claims to have had an affair with one of them. I have come to know Christine Hart well during these last few months. I have asked her many personal questions. I believe that she has almost recovered from the effects of her early childhood. There is still a naivety about her; an innocence, and there is no doubt that she is still a subject for unscrupulousness. The ethics in the treatment of her by the Newspaper was certainly most questionable.

What remains is a most beautiful woman, a little nervous and fractionally tense, but not one who is overly suspicious: One who laughs easily, and speaks with openness and frankness. I think that she can be summed up with the reply she gave me when I asked her if she was happy now . . .

"How can anyone be really happy with all the hunger and distress that there is in the World today?" . . . .

Christine Hart . . . Good luck to you . . . .